PROFILE

OF

OLD NEW ENGLAND

PROFILE

OF

OLD

NEW ENGLAND

Yankee Legends, Tales, and Folklore
by Lewis A. Taft
Illustrated

DODD, MEAD & COMPANY
NEW YORK

Library of Congress Catalog Card Number: 65-10462

Second Printing

Printed in the United States of America
by The Cornwall Press, Inc., Cornwall, N. Y.

To my wife and helpmate, Ruth

Acknowledgments

It is with sincere gratitude that I take this opportunity to thank Mr. Charles Haywood for his kind and thoughtful suggestions which were of the utmost assistance to me in writing this book. I would like to thank my friend Robb Sagendoff, editor and publisher of the YANKEE for his permission to use two legends, namely "The Hanging at Wessaguscus," and "The Legend of Peter Rugg," which were previously published in that magazine. I would also like to thank Mrs. W. A. Christie of the New London Public Library who helped me obtain material for "Bride's Brook," and Richard H. Campbell of Warwick, Rhode Island for his genealogy of the Clapp Family which was helpful in writing the story of "Stonewall Silas Clapp." To the kind and courteous librarians of the Swanton (Vt.), the Weymouth (Mass.), and the Portsmouth (N.H.), Public Libraries, I say thank you. I would also like to acknowledge the help given to me in my research by the librarians of the Providence and the Elmwood Public Libraries of Providence, Rhode Island.

LEWIS A. TAFT

Preface

Here is a selection of legends and anecdotes of Old New England which have lived with great vitality through the years. Some are droll or humorous. Others are grim or sad. Many are informative as well as entertaining.

There are stories of the early New England explorations, of colonial characters, of Indian legends, of witches, pirates, criminals, buried treasures, shipwrecks and haunted houses. They are as varied as the personalities who have, through many generations, told or listened to them. They reflect the profile of Old New England.

A few decades ago, several legend and folklore collectors took the most popular of these yarns, abridged and condensed them without regard to their entertaining values until they became only skeletal remnants of what had been interesting and lively tales.

In this book I have endeavored to recreate these stories in their original form and to recapture the spirit and essence of them as they were narrated by master storytellers. If you derive pleasure from this book, I will have succeeded.

Lewis A. Taft

Contents

Illustrations

Following page 112

LEGENDS OF DISCOVERY,

OF NORSEMEN,

OF PHOENICIANS AND IRISH,

OF VENETIANS, OF SPANIARDS,

OF THE EARLY EXPLORERS, AND

THE STRANGE RUINS

AND WRITINGS FOUND

IN NEW ENGLAND.

The American Saga

Historians generally agree that Norsemen from Iceland and Greenland were the first Europeans to discover America and also that their camps were located somewhere in New England. They visited these shores several times to trade with the natives and to cut wood. Once they tried to establish a colony, but the enmity of the natives finally drove them away. The tales of their voyages were retained, first orally in a series of folk sagas. Later they were collected and printed by an early Icelandic bishop. These are the oldest New England legends.

It was Bjarni Herjulfson, the Iceland trader, who first discovered unknown lands to the south and west of Greenland. It happened in the year A.D. 986. He had returned to Iceland from a voyage to Norway, intending to spend the winter in his father's house, but he found the familiar house and lands in the possession of strangers. From them he learned that his father had sold his estates and followed the outlaw Eric the Red to far-off Greenland.

Bjarni had a one-track mind. He had come to Iceland to spend the winter in his father's house. His father had removed to Greenland. Ergo! He would sail to Greenland and spend the winter in his father's house. No wavering of purpose. Bjarni Herjulfson was a man to admire.

From Iceland he sailed with his stalwart crew and headed west, toward Greenland and a great adventure. The weather drove him off his course—first a drear, thick fog; then an icy north wind, a wind which blew with such fury that the ship was in danger of being engulfed in towering waves. The Norsemen fought the elements. They furled the great sail and dragged sea anchors. For days the wind buffeted their frail craft, driving it southward. Eventually the storm blew itself out and the ship sailed on a sunlit sea.

They sailed toward the west and sighted land, a coast of great sand dunes thinly covered with grass and low bushes. Bjarni knew that it could not be Greenland, for he had been told of the bare mountains and huge glaciers of that country. His crew wanted to land and explore the strange shores. They sought permission from their leader, but he was not interested.

"It is my advice that we only skirt the coast," he told them. After all, Greenland was his destination.

So they left this land behind and sailed for two more days before sighting another land. This was a level country, indented with many bays and inlets. Great trees covered the land, growing to the edge of the water. Again the crew wished to land but Bjarni was interested only in reaching Greenland.

Three days later they sighted a third landfall which proved to be a rocky, mountainous island. They sailed for four more days before arriving at Greenland.

Bjarni Herjulfson settled down on his father's estates and never again ventured to sea. However, the story of his voyage and of the unknown lands he had sighted was told and retold in Greenland households, yet fourteen years went by before another Norse ship set sail to find and explore them.

To Leif Ericson, a fitting whelp of that old pirate Eric the Red, goes the credit for making the first landings on the coast of North America.

Eric was a true Viking. In the year 997 he left his patrimony in Greenland for a voyage to the court of Norway. His crew was a group of gay young adventurers. They sailed to the Hebrides, Ireland and Denmark. They made landings on isolated coasts, plundering when they could, stealing willing and unwilling women, carousing and enjoying life. After a time, they arrived in Norway.

At that particular period the people of Norway were being converted to Christianity by several missionary priests. During their stay the Greenland Vikings were exposed to the teachings of the new religion. Leif Ericson and some of his crew became Christians. When they left Norway to return to their homeland, they carried a priest as a passenger.

After tasting the fleshpots of Europe, the humdrum existence which faced them on their return to Greenland had little appeal to Leif and his adventurers. On the return voyage they often discussed the possibilities of sailing to discover and explore new lands.

A few months after their return, Leif Ericson visited the home of Bjarni Herjulfson and listened carefully to his description of the strange shores he had seen to the south and west of Greenland. Returning to his home, Leif urged his father to lead an expedition to the lands Bjarni had viewed, but the old rover had fallen from his horse and was nursing a badly bruised foot. Eric the Red was a superstitious fellow and perhaps thought the injury was a forewarning of disaster. Whatever the reason, he refused to go aboard the ship. However, he gave Leif his blessings and a witch's charm for luck.

So Leif Ericson, in the spring of 1000, sailed from Greenland with a crew of thirty-five men. They followed in reverse the course taken by Herjulfson. Some distance to the south of Greenland, they made a landfall on a barren shore covered with huge, flat stones. They landed on the bleak shores but stayed only briefly, naming the place Helluland, or "slate-land."

Again they sailed to the south. After several days they saw a thickly wooded coast. They landed and explored the coast. A great forest of trees covered the land. This country they named Markland, or "woodland."

From Markland the explorers set sail and encountered a northeast gale. For two days their ship scudded before a whipping wind. On the third day they sighted land. The wind fortunately abated. Following the coast they came to a place where a river flowed from a large lake into the sea. They sailed into the lake and moored their ship on a sandy shore.

The waters in the lake were alive with fish, and the country appeared so pleasant that Leif decided to spend a winter there. The Greenlanders cut down trees, built sturdy, comfortable huts and explored the adjacent countryside.

One day a south countryman (probably a servant or slave) ran into camp holding bunches of grapes in his hands. The Greenlanders were not familiar with the fruit, but they tasted and found them excellent. It is quite likely that their south countryman also taught them how to press the juices from the grapes to make wine. The saga mentioned that a boatload of grapes were gathered, probably for that purpose. At any rate, Leif Ericson named the country Vinland the Good.

Leif and his men enjoyed their stay in New England. The winter was mild and they had plenty to eat. In the spring they loaded their ship with wood (a precious commodity in Greenland) and sailed back to their homeland. There is no evidence that Leif ever sailed again to his camp in Vinland.

Thorvald Ericson, Leif's brother, was the next Greenland leader to visit Vinland. In the spring of 1005 Thorvald and his crew sailed for the new lands. They succeeded in locating Leif Ericson's camp, where they stayed during the winter months. In the spring they sailed from the camp and explored the coast to the south.

One day Thorvald's shipmaster saw two skin boats turned

bottoms up to provide a shelter for several sleeping natives. Stealthily surrounding the sleeping Indian, the Greenlanders fell upon them with their swords. One swift-footed native escaped; the others were killed.

This stupid slaughter provoked quick reprisal by angry natives. Early the following morning, a horde of Indians in a fleet of canoes attacked the Viking ship. The battle was hot and bloody. The Greenlanders succeeded in repelling the attackers, but in the thick of the fight an arrow penetrated Thorvald's side. Several days later he died from his wound.

The Viking crew buried their chieftain on a prominent headland, covered his grave with a cairn of stones and sailed back to Leif Ericson's camp. Here they spent a second winter. In the spring they returned to Greenland with a cargo of logs.

The third son of Eric the Red, Thorstein Ericson, sailed the following spring for Vinland with a crew of thirty-five Greenlanders. His wife Gudrid accompanied him.

It was an ill-fated voyage. Storms buffeted the ship, blowing it far to the east. Food and water became spoiled by salt spray. Thorstein became ill, and the shipmaster was unable to locate Vinland.

They made a landfall in a desolate land of huge pine trees. Thorstein died and was buried on the shore. Afterwards Gudrid ordered the shipmaster to sail back to Greenland.

Two years later there came to Greenland and Eric the Red's domain a wealthy young trader in a ship loaded with trade goods. His name was Thorfinn Karlsefni.

Eric the Red entertained the young trader and his crew through the long winter months. In Eric's house, Thorfinn met Gudrid, Thorstein Ericson's lovely widow, and promptly fell in love with her. With Eric's approval, the couple were married.

Persuaded by his adventurous bride and the many glowing reports of the fair country to the south, Thorfinn Karlsefni decided to colonize Vinland. Accordingly, in the spring of 1007, he sailed from Greenland with a fleet of four ships carrying 160 men, several women and a number of cattle.

One of the ships was commanded by a Greenlander named Thorvald, who took with him on the voyage his wife Freydis, a dark, passionate woman. Legend claimed that she was the daughter of Eric the Red and an Icelandic witch. She was said to be able to produce spells which ensured favorable weather for her husband's ships.

Perhaps Freydis's charms also favored the expedition, for Karlsefni's small fleet sailed swiftly before northerly winds and over sunlit seas. They found Leif Ericson's camp and built a settlement nearby. That summer Gudrid gave birth to a son, and they named him Snorro.

At first the new settlement prospered. They found the natives eager to trade rich furs for pieces of red cloth and gilded trinkets. The land and waters teemed with game and fish, and they found wild grain growing in abundance. The men worked hard, fishing, hunting, hewing timbers and harvesting grain, grapes and wild berries. The women labored from dawn to darkness curing fish and game for the coming winter.

During the dreary winter months, however, the dark devils of envy and evil passions assailed the Greenlanders. The men quarreled and fought over the women. Some of them kidnapped Indian girls and kept them in their cabins. This propensity for stealing women angered the natives. They stopped all trade and refused to enter the settlement.

One morning early in the spring a horde of Indians attacked the colony. Their surprising onslaught created panic among the Vikings. Many were slain before they could don their armor. The survivors were driven toward the shores of the lake.

Freydis, wife of Thorvald, finding herself surrounded, picked up the sword of a fallen Greenlander. With mad fury she bared her breasts and, screaming wildly, rushed at the Indian warriors. Disconcerted by her berserk attack, the natives suddenly took fright and ran back into the forest.

The battle was over but the losses of the colonists were great. Many of their best men had been killed or wounded and most of their houses burned to the ground.

The Greenlanders spent another year in Vinland, but the enmity of the natives finally compelled them to abandon their settlement. Freydis and Thorvald opposed this move strenuously, but Karlsefni ordered everyone to leave. In 1010 they returned to Greenland.

Soon after the return of Karlsefni's expedition, a ship arrived in Greenland from Norway. It was commanded by two brothers, Helgi and Finnbogi.

They were entertained by Thorvald and Freydis, who told them exaggerated tales of the rich woodlands of Vinland.

Some of the sagas claim that Freydis bewitched the brothers. Perhaps this was so. She did seem to possess a facility for dominating men. At any rate, through her efforts the Norwegian brothers agreed to join Thorvald on a voyage to the new lands.

They sailed from Greenland in the summer of 1011 in two ships. Thorvald's craft was the same one that he had sailed in Karlsefni's expedition and was manned by thirty-five Greenlanders. Helgi and Finnbogi's ship carried a crew of thirty Norsemen and several women.

The ship sailed by the Norwegians was new and swift. It arrived at Vinland long before the old and sluggish craft piloted by Thorvald. They landed and, while awaiting the arrival of the Greenlanders, occupied some of the huts built by the Ericsons.

A few days later Thorvald's ship sailed into the salt lake. Freydis flew into a rage when she discovered that the Norwegians had taken possession of her brother's huts. Her face dark with anger, she ordered them to vacate the premises.

The disgruntled Norsemen, with many harsh words, left the

camp and built other huts a short distance away. Ill-feeling, however, was engendered between the two parties and persisted through the autumn and winter. Helgi and Finnbogi tried to resume friendly relations with Freydis and her husband but Thorvald remained cold and surly toward them. Perhaps he had reasons to resent the presence of the two younger men.

One wintry night Freydis awoke and slipped from the marital bed without disturbing her husband. Barefooted, she hurried across the frozen ground to the Norwegian camp. Stealthily she entered the cabin occupied by the two brothers and awoke Helgi. Motioning him to follow her, she led the way to a deserted cabin midway between the two camps. In the darkness of the neutral hut, Freydis made a sordid proposal to the Norwegian, but he was wary, suspicious of her intent. Bluntly he refused, threatening to reveal her actions to her husband.

"At least we can be friends," she urged.

"What will be, will be," Helgi answered ambiguously and strode from the hut.

Angered by his refusal and frightened by his threat, Freydis hurried to her cabin and awoke Thorvald.

"While you slept this night like a winter bear," she raged, "Helgi the Norwegian dishonored your wife."

Thorvald felt of her cold feet and rage blazed in his heart. Quickly he donned his armor, buckled on his sword and awakened his men. When they were armed, he led them to the opposing camp, where they easily captured and bound the sleepy Norwegians.

The captured men were dragged from their huts and dumped on the ground in front of a hastily ignited bonfire. Thorvald's initial leadership wavered as he gazed at his prisoners.

"What shall we do with them?" he asked Freydis.

"Kill them! Kill them!" his wife urged.

Nodding, he picked up his battle-axe and murdered Helgi

with one blow. The Greenlanders followed his example. With axe and sword, they butchered the Norwegians. Five women were left alive. Thorvald would have spared their lives, but Freydis took her husband's axe and killed them with her own hands.

When the winds of spring had warmed the air, the Greenlanders sailed back to their homeland in the Norwegians' ship. Thorvald's vessel was scuttled. With gifts and threats, Freydis and Thorvald ensured the silence of their crew.

Rumors of the massacre, however, were whispered about, finally reaching the ears of Leif Ericson. He arrested three of Thorvald's crew and put them to the torture until they confessed the whole bloody story.

"I have not the heart to treat my wicked sister and her husband as they deserve," Leif said, "but this I will foretell. They and their children will live and die in evil."

Leif Ericson's forecast came true. Thorvald was drowned. Freydis outlived him for only a few years. Overcome by a fit of madness, she murdered her two children and killed herself.

Freydis, Thorvald and their crew of Greenlanders were the last of the Northmen recorded to have visited Vinland. When Leif Ericson died, the era of Norse explorations came to a close.

Somewhere on the shores of New England are buried the artifacts and bones of many venturesome Norsemen. When the northeast winds whip across these shores, whistling through tall pine trees and moaning around the eaves of houses, perhaps you can hear the ghostly lamentations of those long-forgotten rovers.

When first examined by European historians and geographers, the sagas were dismissed as folktales—fanciful stories dreamed up by Icelandic Norsemen to help pass the long winter evenings. However, as the translations became available to interested persons in many countries, scientific attempts were made to prove or disprove the physical and geographical evidence. It soon became apparent that, in the main, the sagas were true accounts. Leif Ericson and his crew must be conceded the accolade of being the first white men to step on the shores of this continent. They preceded the Great Admiral, Christopher Columbus, by 492 years.

Where did the venturesome Norsemen land? This is a question that has been hotly argued. Suffice to say that most authorities agree that they must have landed on New England's shore.

North Salem's Irish? Ruins

While it must be conceded that Norsemen, according to recognized history, were the first Europeans to tread New England shores, casual and somewhat ambiguous references in ancient manuscripts point to the possibility that other people may have preceded them. Without enough verification to be classified as historical, these tales must be regarded as legends.

To lend substance to these stories, however, there have been found in New England unknown but apparently archaic inscriptions and pictures cut into the hard surface of a few boulders and ledges. One of the most publicized of these is the Dighton Rock, a large boulder lying in tidewater near the mouth of the Taunton River in Massachusetts. Another is the strange petroglyph of a Scottish knight in armor, engraved on a hillside ledge in Westford, Massachusetts.

Also, strange and unusual stone structures have been discovered which defy explanation. In North Salem, New Hampshire, the largest of these, a complex of twenty-two massive stone huts half-buried on a hill, has puzzled archaeologists for many years.

One of these odd structures is divided into three rooms and has the appearance of a crude temple. Nearby, a four-and-a-half-ton slab of granite with deep-cut drainage grooves along

13

the edge has been likened to similar stone artifacts found in the ruins of ancient Phoenician cities of the Mediterranean. These great stone slabs are known to have been used for human blood sacrifices.

Several years ago, Mr. Frank Glynn, a member of the Connecticut Archaeological Society, became convinced that the strange stone structures at North Salem had been built by Phoenicians.

The Phoenicians were a race of seafarers and traders who founded several city-states in the Mediterranean area. The great city of Carthage, mortal enemy of Rome, was a Phoenician nation. They were venturesome sailors. Herodotus, the Greek historian, in 450 B.C. stated that Phoenician ships often voyaged to Albion and Hibernia (ancient names of Britain and Ireland) and also to the Orkneys. A papyrus document found in the ruins of a Phoenician fort in Spain stated that Gaelic slaves under Phoenician taskmasters worked the tin mines in Cornwall, England. If this is true, a number of these Mediterranean people must have resided in Cornwall. Long, low Phoenician galleys with their carved prows and great square sails may have been a common sight along the coasts of ancient France and England.

It is quite conceivable that one or more of these ships may have been driven by storm across the North Atlantic to the shores of New England. If they were shipwrecked, with no means to return to their homeland, they may have built a temple and stone structures such as the ones at North Salem. They would be the people most likely to possess the engineering skill used in constructing such massive edifices.

Picture swarthy, hook-nosed Phoenician adventurers, armed with sword, axe and spear, cased in bronze and leather armor, traveling Indian trails to their stone village on a New England hill. Fantastic? No more so than the idea of American astronauts landing on the surface of the moon.

These same mysterious stone structures at North Salem previously fostered another theory. The late William Goodwin of Hartford, Connecticut, a well-known amateur archaeologist, spent many hours in the1930s, excavating in and around the stone huts. He became convinced that the rock habitations had been built by early Irish Christians, followers of Saint Columba, known as "Culdees."

Mr. Goodwin, following many clues, located the reputed remnants of fifteen unmortared stone huts or cells similar to others found in Ireland which were used by Culdee missionaries.

The Culdees were a sect of early Irish Christians who led a primitive form of monastic life under the direction of an abbot. They built their monasteries in desert places far from towns or cities. Some were on islands in the interior lakes of Ireland; others were located on islands near the coast. Small communities of Christians grew up about these Culdee monasteries, quite apart from the pagan worshippers who ruled the land.

About A.D. 450, When Norsemen raided Ireland, the Culdees fled before them. Some of them went to the Orkneys, the Faroes, the Shetland Island and Scotland. Others fleeing to the west discovered Iceland and founded several monasteries there. Later, when pagan Norsemen found their way to Iceland and began to settle on the island, the Culdees again took flight.

Where did they go from Iceland? It was Mr. Goodwin's belief that they traveled west again to Greenland and from there to New England. On the shores of the Piscataqua River they met American Indians and probably made converts. With the aid of these natives, the Culdees built the massive stone structures at North Salem which became the headquarters for their missionary efforts. From this center, Culdee monks traveled the widespread Indian trails into Massachusetts and Rhode Island, building their stone cells, using them as habitations while they endeavored to convert the natives to Christianity.

How long did they reside here before becoming assimilated by the Indians? Mr. Goodwin believed that the Irish monks lived for several generations among the savages. There are several savants who concur with his theories. A few linguists have proved to their own satisfaction that certain Algonquin Indian words are derived from Gaelic. If this is true, the Culdees must have exerted considerable influence over the native population.

People from Ireland have always possessed an affinity for New England. The Irish have immigrated to these shores from the earliest colonial period. Their descendants have had a large share in developing and shaping the distinctive history of this segment of the United States. It is an amusing thought that they may be able to lay claim to New England by priority of discovery and colonization.

No records of Phoenician voyages to this hemisphere have ever been found, and nowhere have we discovered indisputable archaeological evidence of their presence in New England.

There is a thread of tradition and many old legends to support a thesis that Culdees from Ireland found their way to the coast of America. The historian and geographer John Fiske wrote: "the passion for solitude led some of the disciples of Saint Columba to make their way from Iona to the Hebrides and thence to the Orkneys, Shetlands, Faroes and Iceland where a colony of them remained until the arrival of the Northmen in 874."

There is evidence that they were in Greenland when Eric the Red discovered that island in 863. They seem to have had settlements at Garda on Eriksfirth. Goodwin believed that they left Greenland sometime between 863 and 866. Stone ruins have been found on Sculpin Island off the coast of Labrador which have been attributed to the Culdees. If groups of these Irish monks reached the shores of New England, they antedated the arrival of the Norsemen by many years.

Lord Sinclair and the Zeno Brothers

Another legend of early voyages to New England, this one gleaned from ancient manuscripts, concerns two Venetian brothers: Nicolo, known as the Chevalier, and Antonio Zeno. They were members of one of the oldest and most distinguished families of Venice.

Their father, Pietro Dracone Zeno, was captain-general of the Christian League, a military organization formed to contain and harass the Turks. Their oldest brother, Carlo, won a signal victory in the war against Genoa and was ever after known as the Lion of Saint Mark. Both Nicolo and Antonio Zeno served under their brother in this war.

After peace between the two seafaring cities was established, Chevalier Nicolo Zeno was seized with a desire to visit the distant nations of England and Flanders. He fitted out a ship and, in 1390, left his native city.

Sailing through the Strait of Gibraltar, Nicolo's ship breasted the waves of the great and largely unknown Atlantic Ocean. Keeping in sight of the coast, they sailed northward, blessed by days of fair winds and clear skies.

All good things come to an end. A hatful of clouds developed into a terrific gale. The Venetian ship was carried by towering seas far out into the Atlantic. Captain and crew fought a grim battle with death as days passed in a dreadful discordancy of shrieking wind and hammering seas. Then the gale began to abate. The weary sailors, many of whom had not slept for days, stumbled to their bunks for a much needed rest. Alas, even the watch fell asleep. Without a hand at the helm, the ship was caught in the grips of a strong tide and cast on one of the Faroe Islands. Most of the crew gained the shore and salvaged the ship's stores.

However, this was not the end of their misfortunes. A large group of natives congregated around their camp. The ship's stores aroused their cupidity. Suddenly they attacked the Venetians. Zeno's men fought courageously, but they would have been eventually overwhelmed had it not been for the arrival of a great chieftain with a force of knights and men-at-arms. The newcomers quickly put the natives to flight. This great chief was Henry Sinclair of Roslyn, Earl of the Orkneys.

On discovering Nicolo Zeno's rank and importance, Sinclair treated him with extreme courtesy. In a short time the two leaders became friends.

Sinclair was at that time engaged in conquering the Faroe Islands to add them to his earldom. He had a fleet of thirteen ships and offered command of them to Nicolo. The Venetian accepted.

Zeno seemed to have enjoyed his life in the wild islands. Soon he was sending letters to his brother Antonio telling of his adventures and urging him to come to the Orkneys. Within a year Antonio arrived to join his brother.

Around 1394 Nicolo became interested in the Norse settlements in Greenland. In July of that year he sailed from the Faroes and, in a remarkably swift voyage, arrived in Greenland. In a letter to his brother, he gave a vivid description of conditions in Eric the Red's old domain. He stayed several weeks on the island, but the climate was too severe. He caught a cold that never left him. On his return to the Orkneys he died.

After Nicolo's funeral, Earl Sinclair urged Antonio to take his late brother's post as admiral of the Orkney fleet. Antonio, after some hesitation, accepted.

Five years went by. Then a Norse fisherman was washed ashore on the Faroes. Brought before Earl Sinclair, he told this astonishing story:

"Six and twenty years ago, I with several companions in four small boats ventured far out to sea. Here we became the victims of a storm which blew our frail craft onto a strange coast. The land proved to be Estotiland, an island somewhat smaller than Shetland. The inhabitants were friendly and treated us well, although they spoke a different language.

"However, there lived on the island another European who had also been cast ashore. He could speak Latin. One of my companions was conversant with that language so we were able to make our thoughts known. Our new friend conducted us to the principal city of the island where we lived for several months, observing the people and learning their language.

"The Estotilanders sowed grain and brewed beer. They built ships and worked metal. Although they were a seafaring people and traded with Greenland, they had no knowledge of the loadstone or compass.

"There came a day when the Estotilanders formed an expedition to attack a land to the south known as Drogio. Because of our knowledge of the compass, we were asked to accompany them. This we agreed to do.

"For several days, our fleet of ships sailed south and west until we saw a coastline covered with trees. The captain of the Estotilanders said it was the land of Drogio and we drove our boats onto the shore. Scarcely had we landed before a great army of natives overwhelmed us. The natives were barbarians and cannibals. They killed the Estotilanders and ate their flesh.

Because of our white skin, I and my companions were spared.

"To have possession of white men seemed to give prestige to the tribes. All the neighboring tribes were eager to own us. Soon they began to fight for our possession. Wild battles took place but we were never harmed. We were captured and re-captured, moving from one village to another. This happened over twenty times. In this manner, we were carried far to the west and south. This seemed to be a vast country, aye, a new world.

"The natives of Drogio in the north were uncivilized. They lived on the flesh of animals killed in hunting. They carried bows, and lances and arrows tipped with stone or bone. The natives to the south were more intelligent. They tilled the ground and worked metals.

"After living with these natives for many years, I decided to make my escape. I ran away from the village, traveled for many days through great forests, and swam many rivers. Finally, I arrived at Drogio where I was welcomed by the chief. Here by good luck, I heard that some boats had arrived on the coast. Hurrying to the shore, I was overjoyed to find that the strangers were from Estotiland. Readily they agreed to take me with them. Because of my knowledge of the language of the country, I acted as interpreter for them.

"After making several prosperous voyages with these traders, I decided to return to my own country. I secured a boat and hired two Estotilanders to sail with me. They were drowned when my ship was wrecked on this island."

After listening to the fisherman's story, Sinclair decided to fit out an expedition to visit Estotiland and the great new world beyond. Unfortunately the fisherman, who promised to accompany them, died before the expedition sailed.

About the year 1400 Sinclair's expedition, under command of Antonio Zeno, sailed from the Faroes toward the unknown western reaches of the sea. According to fragmentary writings concerning this voyage, they arrived without incident at the Island of Estotiland. Here Antonio Zeno parted with Earl Sinclair. The Venetian returned to the Faroes while Sinclair, with two ships, continued on toward Drogio and the vast new world seen by the Norse fisherman. No other account of this expedition has ever been found.

Many researchers believe that Zeno's Estotiland must have been Newfoundland. Even at that early date there were permanent fishing settlements on that island. It is easy to believe that these fishermen would augment their incomes by trading. If there is an iota of truth in the fisherman's story, the unknown country to the south must have been the North American Continent. Thus it is conceivable that Sinclair landed on New England shores ninety years before Columbus sailed on the voyage which made him famous. It may also be conceivable that the petroglyph of a Scottish knight carved on a ledge in Westford, Massachusetts, may have been placed there as a memorial of discovery.

Apparently the adventures, discoveries and explorations of Nicolo and Antonio Zeno were well documented—first, by a series of letters written by Antonio to his brother Carlo in Venice; second, by a map and a detailed account of affairs in the northern seas. Unfortunately, Antonio died shortly after his arrival home, and his papers and map gathered dust in the old Zeno palace.

Over a century later, one of the children in the family found the old manuscripts. Playing with them, he tore and mutilated some of them. This child was Antonio Zeno's great-great-great-grandson, Nicolo, born in 1515.

Many years later Nicolo hapened to again find some of the remnants of these papers. There were a few grimy old letters and a map, brittle and faded with age. Sensing their importance, Nicolo pieced together and copied the letters with an explanatory note. He copied the map but made a grave mistake by attempting to amend it so that it might correspond to others of a more recent date. The letters and map were published in a little book about 1558. The map, because of its amendments, was found to be completely inaccurate, thus throwing doubt on the whole story of the Zeno brothers' voyages. Today most historians are inclined to concede that the Zeno brothers' story, in the main, is true.

Tales of the Ambiguous
Dighton Rock

Close to a narrow promontory known as Assonet Neck, where the Taunton River flows into Mount Hope in southern Massachusetts, rests a large boulder which has probably stirred more controversy than any other physical feature in New England. Famous as the Dighton Rock, it is distinguished from thousands of other water-washed boulders by a number of petroglyphs and inscriptions engraved on a plane surface of the rock. Since its discovery in early colonial days, it has evoked the wonder and curiosity of hundreds of people the world over. Cotton Mather, James Winthrop, Dr. Baylies, Ezra Stiles, Benjamin Franklin and George Washington were a few of the eminent citizens who traveled to Assonet Neck to gaze upon the enigmatic rock. Until a short time ago, it had rested in the tidewater where it was nearly inundated at high tide. Now it has been transported to higher ground where it rests in an enclosure.

Researchers have, through the years, given many different interpretations of the strange characters incised on the face of the rock; many theories of their origin have been promulgated from time to time. They have been variously attributed to the Devil, to the Indians, to the Phoenicians, Libyans, Hebrews, Chinese, Norsemen, and finally to a lost Portuguese explorer.

A local legend tells of a farmer who dreamed on three consecutive nights that he had found a chest of gold buried near the base of the Dighton Rock. One moonlight night at low tide he went to the Rock and began digging in the loose gravel at its base. He hurried, knowing well that in an hour the rising tide would force him to leave. In a few minutes his shovel struck against a large object. Quickly he uncovered the edge of a brass-bound chest. As he reached into the excavation to clear dirt from the lid, a sudden rush of water poured over him. He stood up, staring in amazement. The tide was rising rapidly. He could feel the suction of mud and water pulling at his legs. Dropping the shovel in a panic, he waded toward the Neck. Suddenly the moon was hidden by an unearthly mist. A dreadful laugh shattered the stillness. In front of him stood the Devil, tail, horns, cloven hoofs and all. The Devil was beckoning to him. Turning, he ran, sloshing through the water until he reached the shore. Instantly the mist disappeared. The moon shone overhead in all its glory. The man looked back. The ground out to the rock was dry. Well beyond the rock, he could see the receding tide. He never went back to dig for the treasure chest. The Devil had beckoned to him. He had had a close call. He had learned his lesson.

Schoolcraft, that eminent student of the American Indian, voiced a belief that most of the characters graven on the Dighton Rock were petroglyphs—Indian picture writing. At his instigation, an Algonquin Shaman named Chingwauk attempted to read the inscriptions. He succeeded only partially, stating afterward that only a few of the characters were of Indian origin.

A French antiquarian by the name of Edmund Francois Jomard, who studied several copies of the Dighton Rock characters, found them remarkably similar to hieroglyphics found on stones along the ancient caravan routes in North Africa. They were reputed to be figures of an ancient script used by Numidian traders many years before the time of Herodotus.

Several researchers, after examining photographs and copies of the strange engravings on the Rock, believed that some of the characters were scribed by early Phoenician explorers.

One gentleman, Vicomte Don Enrique Onffroy de Thoron, in a book entitled *Les Pheniciens a l'Ile d' Haiti et sur le Americain Continent*, said that Phoenicians made voyages to Haiti and South America. He also said that their ships frequently sailed a northern route past Iceland and Greenland, thence down the coast of North America to Mexico and Central America. He declared that certain characters on the Dighton Rock supply proof of these migrations. De Thoron traced out three of the figures on the Dighton Rock and identified them as the Phoenician letters m, l, n: mâlôn, equivalent to the phrase: "here lies."

He interpreted these letters with several of the hieroglyphic-like characters as forming the sentence: "Here lies one whom we mourn. Seeking to enrich himself, he fought, pillaged and laid waste. His luxurious life passes by like a rapid wave."

The author concluded that the date of these engravings was about 33 B.C.

Mr. Buckingham Smith, a student of Mexican history and antiquities, offered a new interpretation of a portion of the inscription on the rock. After studying a drawing of the characters, he singled out one line which he interpreted as meaning: "Jesu Christo Sonlisimo Jesus Maria Joseph."

Mr. Smith suggested that these inscriptions may have been derived from Spanish missionaries who penetrated the country at a very early period but of whom no records have ever been found.

Another version of the Dighton Rock characters, by a Reverend John P. Lundy, was that the carvings were definitely Mongolian symbolistic writing. He spent a considerable time translating them, finally coming up with the following results:

"A chain or band of folk from the Sunrising (or east), after a long and stormy voyage, found the harbor of a great island. It was wild, uninhabited, green and fruitful. On landing and tying up our boats, we first gave thanks and adoration to God, Shang-Ti, the Supreme Ruler of the Universe. We then sacrificed a human head to the moon, burning it and the body on a round sun-altar. The next morning, a bright sun shone auspiciously on all things below; the heavenly omens and prognostics duly consulted, were all favorable. We then struck across the tangled forest-land westward. Our mouths hankered after something to eat and drink. We found the blue-black maize of our native land and wild fruit. We filled our rice-kettles, we dug a pit under the rocks of a hillside, put in our corn and fruit, and cooked them. We sat down under the shady trees covered with wild grapes and ate our fill. When the moon rose, we retired to our hut or bough-house and slept. The next day we pushed on westward through the tangle, guided by the sun. The Chief gave the order and led the way. We all followed in close march. We crossed some low hills and came to green meadows, filled with wild rice or oats. A stream of water came down from the hills. We stopped; we made a great feast; we sang and danced around our big kettle; its sweet odors curled up high to Shang-Ti, our God and Father in heaven. This memorial stone or altar is dedicated to Shang-Ti, our Ruler and Guide to this newly found island."

This interpretation should place the Reverend Mr. Lundy on a par with those great storytellers Grimms and Hans Christian Andersen.

A theory which found the greatest number of proponents was that many of the characters were of Norseman origin. Professor Charles Christian Rafn, secretary of the Royal Society of Northern Antiquities of Denmark, was the leading advocate of this theory. He studied many drawings of the Dighton Rock writings, and at length came to this country to continue his studies. Aided by Finn Magnusen, a noted authority on ancient runic characters, he came to the conclusion that the engravings were Icelandic and had been carved on the Dighton Rock by a member of Thorfinn Karlsefni's band. He claimed that the land of Hop, mentioned in some of the Icelandic sagas, was situated on the shores of Mount Hope Bay.

So convincing were the Danish savant's arguments that many American students of antiquities came to agree with his conclusions.

However, at least one authority believed otherwise. Edmund Burke Delabarre, a Brown University professor who had made a most thorough and scholarly investigation of the Dighton Rock and the inscriptions thereon, reluctantly dissented with Professor Rafn's theories. Professor Delabarre, over a long period of time, collected every known diagram, sketch and photograph of the rock, also every article he could find which mentioned it. His study of dozens of prints caused him to formulate a different conclusion.

One day while studying a photograph of the rock, he detected among the clusters of characters a date: 1511. No one before had ever noticed it. Careful study of many prints and photographs convinced him that the date was unmistakably on the rock. Yet it could be seen only when the light reflected from the surface of the stone at a certain angle.

The Brown professor then turned his attention to the characters which had been often believed to be alphabetic. Tracing them, he found the letters CORTE. Other letters seemed to have been superimposed in such a way that nothing else could be definitely traced.

Delabarre believed that the date and the letters CORTE were engraved on the surface of the rock by one of the Cortereal brothers, Portuguese explorers who disappeared on voyages to North America in the early sixteenth century.

History tells us that Gaspar Cortereal, in 1501, explored the coasts of Newfoundland and Labrador. Eventually he sent two of his ships back to Portugal while he continued his explorations toward the northwest. On this voyage he disappeared.

In 1502 Miguel Cortereal set sail from Lisbon to search for his missing brother. He sailed with either two or three ships. On reaching Newfoundland, his ships separated in order to explore the area more thoroughly, agreeing to meet again on August 20. The other ships reached the rendezvous on the agreed date, but Miguel's ship failed to appear. His captains waited a fortnight; then running low on provisions, they returned to Lisbon. Nothing was ever heard concerning the fate of Miguel Cortereal. What a strangely coincidental ending to the explorations of the two brothers.

Professor Delabarre believed that the date and figures on Dighton Rock made it possible to entertain the hypothesis that Miguel Cortereal's ship was wrecked somewhere on the New England coast. Somehow he made his way to Mount Hope Bay. Sixty years old, worn with hardships, possibly ill, he might have carved his name and the date on Dighton Rock to attract the attention of some future explorer.

The Pokanokets, an Indian tribe which inhabited southern Massachusetts, have an ancient legend that a great white chief once ruled over the tribe. During his reign the tribe was happy and prosperous. They claimed that he was a God who had come from the east in a winged vessel. Before he died, he prophesied that someday other white men would land on their shores, and he warned his adopted people to treat the white strangers with respect and reverence.

These are a few of the many stories and legends concerning Dighton Rock and its strange inscriptions.

The Curious John Greye Papers

On a cold, windy day in December, 1853, Orlando Green and P. R. Ripley, of Swanton, Vermont, were shoveling sand from a low bank close to the left bank of the Missisquoi River. Their excavation undermined a piece of sod which tore loose from the bank, falling close to their feet. As they glanced down at the sod, the two workers saw a gray, metallic tube in the sand which had been held by the grass roots. It appeared to have been in contact with the earth for a long time. One of the men picked it up and put it in his pocket.

After their load of sand had been delivered to the marble plant at Swanton Falls, Green and Ripley found an opportunity to examine their find. The tube was about five inches long, formed from an irregularly shaped piece of lead. The ends were sealed with a brittle white substance. When the seals were removed, the two men discovered that the tube contained a message written on a piece of heavy paper. The ink used appeared to be a carbon black. The words were written in Elizabethan English. This is the message:

Nov. 29, A.D. 1564.

This is the Salme day, I must die, this is the 90th day since we left the ship, all are perished and on the banks of River I die to, farewelle, may future posteretye know our end.

John Greye.

The discovery of the "John Greye papers" excited interest among historians. The first investigation of the tube and its contents was conducted by Reverend John B. Perry, a local historian. He was assisted by an assayer and a noted professor of history. Both of these men were from Boston. They questioned both Green and Ripley concerning the circumstances of the discovery. They had the paper examined and the substance used to seal the tube analyzed, then announced their belief that the tube, paper and message were undoubtedly authentic.

Later, as so often happens in new archaeological discoveries, another group of so-called authorities investigated the find and labeled the whole affair a hoax. Unfortunately the general public accepted their verdict as the truth.

John Perry rejected their findings, pointing out that they had conducted their investigation many months after the tube had been found by Green and Ripley. During those many months the tube and paper had passed through the hands of many curious people before their re-examination.

Furthermore, the Reverend Mr. Perry, in several papers written on the subject, advanced a fascinating theory. He suggested that John Greye and his companions may have been members of one of Sir Martin Frobisher's expeditions to discover the Northwest Passage. If this theory was correct, John Greye and his companions had been the first Englishmen to traverse land which is now a portion of New England.

Actually, very little is known concerning Frobisher's explorations. History states that he made three attempts to reach India by sailing west. He is credited with having explored the coast of Labrador north to the waters around southern Greenland. By some accounts, he was familiar with the seas around Newfoundland and the islands further west. He also must have known of Jacques Cartier's discovery of the mighty St. Lawrence. Would it not be logical to suppose that he would wish to explore the great stream, to find out if this was the fabled strait to the Indian Ocean? Not caring to risk his ships, he may have sent a pinnace with a small crew to explore and take soundings.

John Greye was an educated man. He would have been the commander of such a crew. Led on by the bright star of adventure, the small group of explorers may have sailed as far west as the rapids near the present site of Montreal. Perhaps they even climbed the steep elevation of the mountain later known as Mont Real. If so, they observed the great forests extending for miles in every direction, a thrilling experience—an experience that some years later would excite the explorer Samuel de Champlain.

They must have left the mighty St. Lawrence and traveled south. Perhaps they gazed with wonder on the clear water of Missisquoi Bay and Lake Champlain. Then fate, having led them so far, finally deserted them. Either sickness or Indian attacks reduced their ranks until only John Greye remained, a white man in an alien wilderness.

How long did he wander alone? No one will ever know. Lost and whipped by the bitter winds of early winter, he kept walking until exhaustion dragged him to a halt, one chore to perform before the end. He fashioned a crude tube from a piece of lead. In his pocket was a bit of paper, once used to protect a brass hinge. The feather of a bird was his quill. Carefully he wrote his message. He signed his name for the last time: John Greye. He may have been a man of renown in his day. If so, his fame is buried under the drifting sands of time. In this generation he is only a mysterious figure of the past.

Placing the message in the tube, he sealed the ends with pine pitch. The cold of November pricked his flesh with tiny needles. Darkness dimmed the earth. He walked a short distance and sat down with his back against a tree, awaiting death. The frigid wind sifted snow over him. Dropping the tube from freezing hands, he arose and staggered through the gloom until he stumbled—and fell for the last time.

The lead tube containing his message, covered by the leaves of many seasons, became a prisoner of the sod. Then time and chance sent a pair of laborers to discover it and bring the message to the eyes of the world. How can one doubt it.

> . . . I die to, farewelle, may future posteretye know our end.
> John Greye.

The date on the John Greye papers cast doubt on the theory advanced by the Reverend Mr. Perry. Excerpts from the record of one of Sir Martin Frobisher's voyages, printed in London in 1600, is as follows:

> The first voyage of M. Martine Frobisher to the northwest for the search of the strait or passage to China, written by Chris. Hall, Master of the *Gabriel*.
>
> In the year of our Lord 1576, the 7th of June being Thursday, the two barks, the *Gabriel* and the *Michael*, and our pinnaces sailed from Ratcliff.

However, there is also a chance that Chris. Hall's date of departure was subject to an error in printing, something that happened often in the early days of the printing press.

LEGENDS AND TALES

OF SAVAGES, HEROISM, MURDER,

OF SHIPWRECKS, OF LOVE AND

PIRATES AND OF DEADLY DUELS.

Hanging at Wessaguscus

Justice gives sentence many times
On one man for another's crimes.
Our brethren of New England use
Choice malefactors to excuse,
And hang the guiltless in their stead,
Of whom the company has less need.
                    SAMUEL BUTLER in "Hudibras."

With many misgivings, tall gentlemanly Edward Johnson stood
under the bare, spectral branches of the white oak tree on
Hunt's Hill, overlooking the small settlement of Wessaguscus
(Weymouth, Massachusetts). The members of the colony
were grouped in front of him, shivering in the bitter wintry
wind that swept over the hill. A sorry dispirited company, he
thought. Weak, cold and half-starved, they could put up little
resistance if the Indians were to attack them.

Savagely he kicked at a stone as if it were fate, then raised
his eyes to glance at the group of Indian warriors clustered at
the edge of the clearing, watching the small band of colonists.
The threat of an Indian attack hovered over the settlement,
and only firm, judicious action by the company could avert it.

Fate had placed Edward Johnson in an unenviable position,

37

for in this dangerous situation he was the judge and temporary leader of the Wessaguscus colony. And this day he must sentence a member of the company to the gallows. A man must hang for stealing from their Indian neighbors. It was late winter in the year 1623.

A short time after the Pilgrims landed at Plymouth, a wealthy London merchant named Thomas Weston had organized a group of colonists and sent them to America in two small ships. This same Thomas Weston had been instrumental in dispatching the Pilgrims to New England in the *Mayflower*, and there are reasons to believe that this new group of colonists were sent to New England in 1622 to reinforce the manpower of the Plymouth colony, which had been depleted by sickness and death.

The Pilgrims objected to the newcomers landing at their colony, so the Weston company landed north of Plymouth at a place called by the Indians Wessaguscus.

Weston's men exchanged gifts with the local Indian sachem, then selected a site for their settlement on a peninsula at the mouth of the Monatiquot River. Industriously the new colonists constructed a blockhouse, some cabins for storing goods and others to live in, surrounding the whole settlement with a stockade.

The company had landed in August, too late to plant crops, so they were forced to depend on the inadequate store left by the ships. Few of the colonists were proficient in hunting or fishing, so they soon depleted their store of food.

The new colony had an able and resourceful leader in Richard Green, a counterpart of Plymouth's energetic Myles Standish. Green led two expeditions, composed of men from both Plymouth and Wessaguscus, to trade with the Indians for food. The friendly Indian Squanto acted as their interpreter.

They were moderately successful on the first expedition, but on the second trading venture their shallop capsized, throwing them into the water. Richard Green and Squanto never recovered from this mishap. They died soon after, probably from pneumonia.

The leadership of the Wessaguscus colony now devolved on an irresolute gentleman by the name of John Saunders or Sanders. He soon proved himself unable to provide the kind of leadership needed by the company.

The winter advanced and the plight of the little colony became desperate. The colonists bartered most of their personal possessions to the Indians for food. Soon they had nothing left but their weapons. Without trade goods, the natives refused to give them food.

As the colonists became weakened by hunger, the Indians, losing their fear of white men, became arrogant and bold. One Indian warrior threatened to kill a woman of the company and went unpunished. But a colonist found guilty of stealing from the natives was publicly flogged. To curb the more enterprising of the starving settlers, John Saunders decreed that the next man who stole from the Indians would be hanged by the neck until dead.

Shortly thereafter the local Indians became so threatening that it was decided to send to Plymouth for military assistance. The colony became a haven of fear. Fear of death at the hands of their savage neighbors even transcended their fear of death from starvation. The men stayed close to the blockhouse, too frightened to dig for shellfish or to go hunting in the forest.

John Saunders, in spite of the danger of winter seas and the threat of an Indian attack on the settlement, embarked on the colony's shallop and sailed for the coast of Maine in the hope of obtaining food from the fishing settlements. He left Edward Johnson as the leader of the unhappy colonists.

A short time later, one of the bravest men in the Wessaguscus colony ventured into the forest to hunt for deer. On the banks of the river he found a large Indian storage pit filled with corn.

He took the corn, brought it into the settlement and divided it among his fellow colonists.

When the Indians discovered the rifled storage pit, they hurried to the blockhouse and demanded that the thief be handed over to them for execution. Edward Johnson refused but promised the angry natives that the culprit would be punished speedily by his fellow colonists. Quickly he ordered the drums beat for assembly.

The colonists gathered on Hunt's Hill. Indians from the nearby village grouped on the edge of the clearing, their attitude both angry and truculent. Johnson explained to the company the reason for the assembly and requested the guilty person to step forth that his actions might be judged. A strong young man of the company, a cobbler by trade, stepped in front of his comrades and in a loud voice admitted that he had taken the corn from the Indian storage pit.

"I took the corn and distributed it to our people that they might not die of hunger," he said. "Why worry you about the Indians' corn when your people are starving. Only two men of our company have dared to hunt in the forest. Unless more diligence is shown in procuring food, our people will all die before the ships arrive from England in the spring."

"What you say about our lack of diligence is true," Johnson answered him. "But the thievery of the Indian corn could cost the lives of everyone in our company. The savages are many and we are few. They can easily overwhelm us. Under these circumstances, you were ill-advised to steal from them. The Indians are demanding a victim for the loss of their corn. If one is not soon forthcoming, I am afraid that they will attack us."

"Find your victim then but do not expect me to sacrifice my life," the young man said angrily. "I took the corn from the heathen, and I do not feel at fault." Sturdily he walked to the huge oak tree and stood with his back against it, glaring defiantly at Johnson.

His fellow colonists looked with troubled countenances from their leader to the cobbler. They hoped that the judge would not command them to disarm the malefactor, for he was a person that could be a Samson in his wrath. Moreover, many of them had eaten some of the stolen corn and felt a kinship in guilt with the young cobbler.

In their dilemma, a young carpenter stood forth from his fellows and urged the judge and his fellow colonists not to allow the complaint against the sturdy young man. Said he, "We can ill afford to lose the services of the only cobbler in the colony."

Now there was in the company a certain woolsorter, a widower and childless, an argumentative, contentious man who had always been loud in his criticisms of those in authority but short in the performance of his duties to the company. He now stood forth from the assembly and, in a voice like the braying of an ass, branded the colonists as a group of ungodly sinners who would condone acts of thievery against their brothers and neighbors, the poor Indians. To his way of thinking, the cobbler had sinned and should be hanged, otherwise the natives would become angered by the dilatory actions of the assembly and murder them all.

Other members of the company stepped forward, the majority of them in favor of showing mercy to the accused, but as soon as one finished his speech, the woolsorter would cry out in a shrill voice, calling them sinners and demanding that the assembly hang the cobbler.

Then a gentleman of the company, a droll quick-witted rogue named Thomas Morton, stepped from the group and bowed to Edward Johnson. He spoke somewhat as follows: "It has been told by many that this cobbler is exceedingly valuable to this company, but the woolsorter is also right in one respect. If we do not punish anyone, the natives are apt to attack us. We cannot withstand such an attack. Therefore, we must produce a victim to mollify the savages. I propose that we forget the guilt of our friend the cobbler. He is a valuable man. Let us pick for a victim a man without kith nor kin, a man who eats much but provides little, a person of no value to our company. Gentlemen! I gaze upon this assembly and see hunters and fishermen, carpenters and coopers, a cobbler, a tanner, a tailor, a smith, all valuable to the welfare of our company. We also have this fellow, a woolsorter. But alas, we have no wool. He hath no kith nor kin nor has he dependents. Gentlemen, I urge that this man be hanged. Not because of any guilt on his part but because he will occasion us little loss. We have very little time for debate. The savages are waiting for a victim."

At the end of Morton's speech there was a chorus of amens. Members of the company laid hold of the poor woolsorter and looked toward their judge, Edward Johnson, for confirmation of the verdict.

This was Edward Johnson's moment of decision, but like Pontius Pilate he washed his hands of the proceedings by turning his back on the assembly.

One can picture Edward Johnson standing alone on Hunt's Hill, long after the colonists and Indians departed. What bitter thoughts must have passed through his mind as the cold wind whistled in the branches of the oak tree, fluttering the clothing on the stiffening body of the woolsorter. Then picture Edward Johnson, a victim of expediency, walking down the hill and out of the realm of recorded history.

Hanging by proxy was first mentioned in *New England Canaan* by Thomas Morton, which was published in England in 1632. Later it was satired in *Hudibras*, a poem published in 1663 by Samuel Butler. A version of this incident was printed in *Voyages* by Captain Wring. Bradford, in his *History of the Plimoth Plantation,* mentioned a hanging at Wessaguscus.

Whether this incident took place is conjectural. One can only observe that where there has been so much smoke, there must have been some flame.

The Ordeal of Hannah Dustin

It was March in the Merrimack Valley, a month of windy, chilly, damp days, of snow and sleet, rain and fog. In the frontier village of Haverhill in that year of 1697, the inhabitants went about their customary pursuits somewhat daunted by the weather and a threat of Indian attacks caused by an early break-up of ice in the river. In the spring when the streams were open, parties of Abenaki warriors, armed with French muskets, often descended the Connecticut and Merrimack Rivers to raid and burn the crude cabins of the English settlers. The settlement of Haverhill had suffered casualties every year for a decade.

In 1690 the province of Massachusetts had supplied a score of soldiers to aid the settlers in manning their six garrison houses where the villagers congregated at any threat of attack. This aid had been continued in subsequent years and was helpful in discouraging small war parties from attacking such strongpoints. However, they were almost useless against the quick hit-and-run raids on homes situated on the outskirts of the settlement. A bell hung outside the meetinghouse was used to alert the inhabitants to possible danger, its ringing tones the tocsin for the valley. Even the smallest toddler had been taught to hurry to the nearest garrison house when it rang.

In 1697 Colonel Nathaniel Saltonstall was commander of the Haverhill defenses. He was a well-educated man of great influence in Massachusetts and a leading citizen of Haverhill. He was town clerk for many years and served as delegate for the town on many occasions. His integrity was beyond question, but his military ability was questionable.

Early in the morning of March 15, a horseman rode into the town and reported to the colonel that a hunter had sighted a party of Indians on the river. It was presumed to be a small hunting party. Then Colonel Saltonstall also did some presuming. He presumed that the Indians were members of a friendly tribe, so he made no effort to warn the settlers, alert the garrisons or send scouts out into the encircling forests. To do the man justice, never before had hostile Indians descended the Merrimack River during the spring floods.

In the farmhouse of Thomas Dustin on the western outskirts of Haverhill, a baby had been born to his wife Hannah in the early hours of morning. It was her eighth child. Now as a weak sun rose over the hills to warm the dank air, Hannah lay on her bed holding the baby close to her body, trying to keep it warm, for the small bedroom was bitter cold. A neighbor, widow Mary Neff, a sallow-complexioned, rawboned but kindhearted woman, was tending the house, keeping watch on three of the youngest Dustin children. The farmer Thomas Dustin with his older children was clearing a field, laboriously prying rocks from the soil and, with the aid of a sledge drawn by his one horse, transporting them to the edge of his land. Suddenly, unobserved by the farmer and his children laboring in the field, a file of Indians, hideously daubed with war paint, emerged from the forest and ran to the farmhouse.

Mary Neff was pushing a log into the large fireplace when the savages burst into the kitchen. Her piercing scream frightened the little Dustin children. Like a trio of rabbits they dodged around and between the legs of the Indians, avoiding clutching hands, and ran screaming toward the field where their father was at work. Four of the raiders pursued them.

Thomas Dustin was instantly transformed into a hero. Hearing the screams of his youngsters, he grabbed his musket, cut the traces between horse and sledge, leaped upon the beast and rode to the rescue. The sight of his three smallest children running toward him, closely pursued by four savage warriors, was enough to cause the bravest man to quail. But Dustin was more than an ordinary man at that moment. He was a father protecting his young. Riding between the riders and his children, he brought the horse to a halt, his musket pointing toward the savages. Daunted by this stern white man astride the big plow horse, the Indians halted and fired a hasty volley at him. The four bullets missed their mark. The steady musket in Dustin's hands was a death warrant. Deciding to seek easier and safer prey, the savages turned and ran back to the farmhouse. Marshaling his children behind him, Thomas Dustin retreated toward the nearest garrison house, convinced that his wife and the widow Neff had been slain.

Meanwhile, in the farmhouse, one of the invaders had struck Mary Neff a glancing blow with his tomahawk, felling her. Two other warriors entered the bedroom where Hannah cowered on her bed. The covers were pulled off of her and thrown on the floor. One of the scowling Indians seized the newborn baby by its heels and dashed its brains out against the wall. In a state of shock over the murder of her baby, Hannah Dustin was pulled from her bed. Barefooted, clad only in a long nightgown, she was pushed into the kitchen and fell on the floor beside Mary Neff, who was leaning against a chair, holding her hands over her bleeding head. The two frightened women crept together and watched in an agony of spirit as the Indians ransacked the house, wantonly destroying everything they could not carry. They allowed Hannah to dress, but so hastily that she was forced from the house with only one shoe on. Then they set fire to the structure.

In many sections of Haverhill, similar scenes were taking place. The Indians had attacked in force. Many of the settlers escaped to the garrison houses, which the raiders did not attack. Others, twenty-seven in all, were killed. Thirteen were taken captive. Among these were Mary Neff and Hannah Dustin. The attack lasted only a short time. Then the raiders with their captives and loot vanished into the forest. The survivors, shocked by the awful calamity which had befallen so many of their loved ones, were unable to initiate a pursuit of the savages. Sadly they buried their dead and began the drear task of reconstruction.

The Indian war party, loaded down with loot and hampered with prisoners, began their long march back to their villages in northern New England. They followed the Merrimack River, hunting and fishing along the way. With little cohesion, the party gradually split up into small bands, each setting its own pace as they traveled northward.

Hannah Dustin, Mary Neff and another captive, young Samuel Lenorson, with four warriors, a squaw and six Indian children, were in a group commanded by a sachem who spoke both French and English. Young Lenorson had been captured in an earlier raid at Worcester.

The squaw gave Hannah a pair of moccasins to wear, not for any altruistic reasons but only to prevent her from becoming lame. The sachem exercised his knowledge of English by detailing to his captives the terrible tortures practiced on English prisoners by the members of his tribe. Thus, mentally harassed and physically exhausted by poor food and privation, the captives were in a state bordering insanity when the Indian band camped for the night on an island near the confluence of the Contoocook and Merrimack Rivers. They had been on the trail for forty-five days.

As the three white prisoners were eating their meager evening meal, Hannah surreptitiously showed the others a tomahawk which she had managed to steal from one of the warriors.

It must have been a grim and dramatic scene—two tattered, wild-eyed women with unkempt hair and a frightened youth, the campfire reflecting red on the surrounding foliage as they stared at the tomahawk. In low tones, Hannah proposed a method of escape, a plan so grim that her companions scarcely breathed as they listened to the details. Before leaving the fireside, they had all agreed to do their part.

Early in the morning of April 29, Hannah Dustin silently crept from her bed of pine boughs. It was dark. The only sounds were the rippling waters of the river, a few distant calls of night birds, and the snore of the Indian squaw. Picking up her stolen tomahawk, she felt her way to a hollow where Mary Neff and young Samuel awaited, shivering with fear and excitement. A brief whispered command and the pair followed her as she crawled to the side of two of the sleeping warriors. Hannah killed them, splitting their skulls with the tomahawk. Mary and Samuel appropriated their weapons. Then with remarkable ferocity, the three captives crawled from Indian to Indian killing them silently and efficiently. The squaw, although badly wounded, escaped in the darkness. To add horror to the macabre deed, Hannah Dustin, Mary Neff and Samuel Lenorson scalped their victims.

With Indian guns and tomahawks, and ten bloody scalps rolled up in a deerskin, Hannah and her accomplices began their long trip down the river to Haverhill. With wonderful luck they accomplished the return trip without meeting with any misadventures from Indians or wild animals.

What a stir they must have occasioned when they arrived at Haverhill, three gaunt scarecrows who had escaped from the valley of death.

A sequel to this story was the action of the General Court

of Massachusetts in voting to give Hannah Dustin twenty-five pounds, Mary Neff twelve pounds ten shillings, and the youth Samuel Lenorson a like sum of twelve pounds ten shillings for the scalps of public enemies.

The Killing of Mogg Megone

In the great wilderness of Maine during the stirring years of the Indian wars and for many years afterward, it would have been difficult to find a more contemptible person than the miserable Indian half-breed known as "Bones" Bonython. He was a liar, a cheat, a murderer and a renegade. In his youth he had been the servant of an English officer whom he envied and hated. When the country became afire with bloody warfare between the French and Indians and the English, Bonython skulked in a garrison house where his master was commander of defenses, and planned dark deeds of betrayal.

One morning he found his chance. Through a loophole he saw a party of Indians creeping toward the fortified house. Only the sentinel on duty by the main door was awake. Sneaking behind the man, Bonython stabbed him to death, then opened the door to the advancing savages. Because of this wretched deed, the Indians spared his life. Later, he laughed when the reveling victors tossed the mutilated body of his master into the flames of the burning garrison house.

After this act of treachery, afraid of English revenge, he had lived for many years in the lodges of the Abenaki. Even his Indian hosts did not trust him. However, they tolerated him, allowing him to build a cabin on the outskirts of their town of Norridgewock.

Later, Bonython married an Indian squaw. He treated her so brutally that she died while giving birth to a baby girl.

Some strange quirk induced the renegade to bestow on his daughter the English name of Ruth. Then he vanished into the forests and was gone for several months. He felt no inclination to spend his time rearing a child.

Several kindhearted squaws nursed and cared for the baby. They brought her to a French Jesuit priest who conducted a mission in Norridgewock. The priest baptized the child and gave the Indian women a blanket to wrap the little motherless girl in. When Ruth grew older, the priest allowed her to attend the mission school where she learned to speak French.

Years went by. Ruth Bonython grew up to young womanhood, well versed in Indian customs and lore but knowing nothing of the Englishmen and their settlements on the banks of the Kennebec below Norridgewock.

When the girl was sixteen, Bones Bonython knifed a young sachem of the Merrimacks in a drunken brawl. The Abenaki chiefs, after due deliberation, banished him from their town.

This was no hardship. The half-breed had few possessions to worry about. With a pack of inferior furs on his back he set out for the English settlements, trusting that time had effaced his treacherous deed. Like a well-behaved squaw, Ruth trudged along the trails behind her father, carrying all her household tools in a pack strapped to her shoulders.

When the pair reached the fort and trading post at Woolwich, Bonython sold his furs and decided to settle in the vicinity. A mile from the English settlement, on the banks of the Kennebec River, the half-breed built a bark and sod shelter. With an axe stolen from the trading post, he made rude furnishings and fashioned a dugout canoe from a giant pine tree which had been felled by lightning. He earned a scant living by fishing and trapping, spending most of his money for rum.

As so often happens in nature, ugly, mean and unprepossessing persons produce offspring of more than ordinary comeliness. Such was the case with Bonython. His daughter Ruth was a strikingly beautiful girl. She was slender and shapely, with large brown expressive eyes, full ruby lips and a shy friendly smile that captured the hearts of all who looked upon her. Her skin, unlike most "breeds," was very light; a light gold through which the pink of perfect health shone with a soft luminosity. In the villages of the Abenaki, many an Indian brave had felt his heart leap when Ruth Bonython smiled. In the large trading post of Woolwich she produced the same effect on the young Englishmen.

Master Tom Scammon, tall, blond and handsome, the only son of the armorer of Woolwich, met Ruth as she was gathering herbs on the river bank. It was love at first sight. Thereafter, scarcely a day went by without the couple meeting either on the river banks or within the walls of the fort. The girl knew few words in English, but language was not necessary. The warmth of a glance, the touch of a hand, spoke love's messages far more eloquently than words.

Master Scammon told his father of his passion for the half-breed's daughter. He brought the girl to his home, introducing her to his parents. They loved her and gave their consent for a marriage in the near future.

One day Bones Bonython, paddling down the Kennebec, spied his daughter and young Scammon walking hand-in-hand on a path by the river. With the morality and deviousness of a snake, he went ashore and crept behind trees and brush to observe them. It did not take him long to realize that his daughter and the young Englishman were in love.

This was not to the half-breed's liking. He had other ideas for Ruth's future. Lately he had been evolving a scheme which would make him a wealthy man. However, it would be necessary to sacrifice his daughter's future to effect the success of his plan.

Bonython had noticed that Englishmen were greatly concerned over the legality of owning land. English courts insisted that every man must possess a legal title to his property. The majority of these deeds were based on early transfers of large tracts of land purchased from local Indian sachems or on confiscation after conquest. Yet a large section of land lying between the Androscoggin and Kennebec Rivers was being settled by the English without title or documentary proof that it had ever been legally purchased from the natives who still lived in the interior. If a man could produce an authentic record of the purchase of this land from a well-known sachem, he would soon be rich. Most of the present occupants of the land would pay handsomely to retain their property. Even at this late date, such a document might be obtained. Mogg Megone, half-brother of the great chief Madockawando, ruled a band of Abenaki living on the banks of Lake Cobbosseecontee. He had once signed a treaty of peace with Governor Phips of Massachusetts. His signature on a bill of sale would likely be honored by English courts.

Fat, dirty, sly Mogg Megone loved rum and pretty women. He had once seen Ruth Bonython in Norridgewock. He had offered to buy her from Bones for a bale of beaver skins. The sachems of the Indian town frowned on the transaction and placed the girl in the custody of the priest until Mogg Megone left the town. Perhaps Megone still wanted the girl. Perhaps for Ruth and a few bottles of rum he would sign a quitclaim to the land.

One morning Bones Bonython placed a jug of rum in the bottom of his canoe and headed upriver. He intended to settle a deal with Mogg Megone. He traveled fast. In three days he reached the Abenaki village on the shores of Lake Cobbosseecontee. The same night he sat in the lodge of Mogg Megone, watching the chief guzzle rum. When Megone was sufficiently under the spell of the liquor, Bonython spoke.

"Give to me all the land which lies between the Androscoggin and the Kennebec and I will give you all the rum you can drink."

The Indian sachem shook his head. "No!"

"Four jugs of rum and my daughter Ruth as your squaw!"

Mogg Megone's lecherous eyes glowed. In the rum-fumed recesses of his mind he savored the delights of holding such a beauty in his arms.

"Good! Good!" he grunted. "I will do it."

Bones tried to persuade him to sign a bill of sale for the land, but the drunken sachem was cautious. "I will not place my mark on your papers now," he told the half-breed. "I must be certain that you will not cheat me."

Bonython was forced to accept this decision, but he urged the Indian to make haste.

"Come to my cabin in Woolwich on the day of the full moon. There I shall give you my daughter Ruth and four jugs of rum."

Mogg Megone nodded solemnly. "Good!" he intoned. Lifting the jug to his lips he took a deep swallow, ignoring the trickle of rum which dribbled from the corners of his mouth onto his greasy buckskin shirt.

It was a week later. Mogg Megone, hurrying along the river trail near the white man's town of Woolwich, saw movement on the path ahead. Like a serpent he glided into a thicket. Cautiously he peered through an opening between the branches. Savage rage boiled within him when he saw Ruth Bonython, whom he already considered his own, walking hand-in-hand with handsome Master Scammon. The lovers paused in front of the Indian's hiding place. A long kiss, a quick embrace and they parted. Ruth ran down the path along the river's edge toward her home. Scammon stood by the thicket watching the girl's lithe, graceful form blend into the shadows of the forest.

Mogg Megone stealthily crept from his hiding place. His

moccasins made no more noise than would the pattering feet of a wood mouse, as he stepped close to his victim. Face contorted with maniacal fury, he raised his tomahawk and sank the sharp blade into the head of the young Englishman. Then utering a savage cry of triumph, he pulled a knife from his belt and deftly scalped the still shuddering white corpse.

That same evening, there came a whisper, a scratch at the door of Bonython's cabin. When Ruth opened the door, Mogg Megone, like a dark, evil shade, slipped into the room. Bones greeted him in the Abenaki tongue and placed the bill of sale with four jugs of rum on the table.

The sachem ignored them. Snatching Ruth's hand, he pulled her close to his reeking body, his burning eyes desecrating her.

"When I place my mark on that paper, you will become my squaw. You will follow me to my lodge."

She twisted away from him. "No!" she protested. "Soon I am going to marry Master Scammon."

"Are you speaking of the man you embraced on the river trail?" the Indian asked.

The surprise and fright mirrored on the girl's face were his answer.

Mogg Megone grinned, his evil countenance shining redly in the light from the tallow-dip candle. "Here is your Master Scammon."

From under his blanket he produced the still bloody scalp of her lover.

"You are mine—and mine alone. Your father has sold you to me."

Ruth stared at the scalp in the Abenaki's hand. The long blond hair of young Scammon which she had so admired was flecked with his blood. This was not an evil dream. It was so. That Indian monster had murdered her beloved Englishman. Suddenly, with the speed of a striking wildcat, she leaped at the grinning killer. Wrenching his knife from its sheath, she stabbed him again and again. Blood poured from his mouth and he collapsed on the floor. Dropping the knife on the table, Ruth gave her father a glance of loathing and ran from the house.

When the body of Tom Scammon was found by hunters from Woolwich they blamed the murder on the French-controlled Abenaki Indians at Norridgewock. Fear, hate and revenge, festering sores in a wilderness no one could call their own, cried out for a war of extermination. The settlers formed an army under the leadership of two noted Indian fighters, Captains Harmon and Moulton. Ten days after the murder of young Scammon, the army began the long march to the Falls of the Kennebec and the town of Norridgewock.

"When we attack the town, kill everything that walks or crawls," were the orders of the two commanders.

Meanwhile, Ruth Bonython, stricken with grief over the loss of her beloved Englishman and stunned by the perfidy of her father, wandered alone along wilderness trails, little caring whether she lived or died. On her conscience, like a leaden weight, was the killing of Mogg Megone. "Vengeance is mine!" said the Lord. She had committed a deadly sin. Her thoughts strayed to the little mission in Norridgewock, and the kindhearted black-robed priest. To him she should confess her sins. The thought gave her a purpose. Without food or weapons, Ruth walked along the river trail toward Norridgewock, knowing not that a short distance behind her an English army was marching with a different purpose, resolved to wipe out the last major community of Abenaki Indians in the eastern part of Maine.

Father Rasles in his chapel at Norridgewock was interrupted in his prayers by a girl who entered the church, her clothing torn and muddy, her face etched with sorrow.

"Father, I have killed Mogg Megone for murdering the man I loved," she confessed.

"My poor sister," he said, compassion in his voice. "Pray! Pray to God and ask his forgiveness."

The half-breed's daughter knelt before the altar and tried to pray. When she closed her eyes, she envisioned the frightened face of Mogg Megone as the knife in her hand cut the life from his body.

"Father, forgive me." Now she thought of the smiling countenance of Tom Scammon, her beloved. She could feel his presence. He was beckoning to her.

"Father, forgive me." From somewhere nearby came a scattering volley of gunfire. Instantly the town became transformed into a bedlam of battle. The wild screams of frightened squaws and the defiant war cries of Abenaki warriors merged with the savage shouts of the English attackers. A group of Indians ran into the chapel, closely followed by a squad of Englishmen. Father Rasles was killed trying to defend his Indian charges. With sickening efficiency, the white soldiers slaughtered the Indians and set the church on fire.

At eventide Norridgewock was a scene of carnage. Few of the Indians had escaped. The church and a score of lodges had been burned to the ground. The armorer of Woolwich, his heart dying within him at the loss of his son and the terrible revenge his countrymen had visited on the Abenaki, walked through the still smoldering town. Near the ashes of the chapel he saw the body of a young woman, her sightless eyes staring at the sky. He paused, struck with a sense of familiarity. Even in death the girl was beautiful. Recognition sent a chill coursing down his spine. It was Ruth Bonython, the little half-breed girl who had been betrothed to his son. Why had she left Woolwich after the death of Tom Scammon? Why had she come here to Norridgewock? It did not matter. His son had loved her.

Tenderly the armorer picked up the body of Ruth Bonython and carried it to the banks of the river. There she was buried by the English soldiers, buried beside the stream where she had known the greatest measure of both joy and sorrow.

This is an old story. It is mentioned briefly in *Myths and Legends of Our Own Land*, by Charles M. Skinner. However, I could not find enough information to verify its historical veracity. The historical background is correct. Bones Bonython may have been the son of Richard Bonython, who was deeded a large tract of land on the east bank of the Saco River in 1630.

The Sagamore Mogg was a Christian Indian, baptized by a French missionary. Possibly, Megone was his Christian name. Herbert Edgar Holmes, a Maine historian, claimed that Mogg was reported killed in the attack on Norridgewock. However, by delving through records of that period, it is difficult to ascertain whether the report of his death was related to the fight or to events leading to the Norridgewock expedition.

The Wreck of the *Palatine*

On a warm day in August, 1738, six hundred and forty German Palatines from the Rhenish Palatinate knelt on a busy wharf in Rotterdam to receive benedictions from their spiritual leaders.

Two ships, their tall masts and spars towering above the kneeling assembly, rubbed restlessly against their mooring lines as if eager to leave the malodorous river banks for the clean, salty reaches of the sea. These were the vessels which had been chartered to carry the emigrating Palatine families across the broad Atlantic to a brave new world which the English had named Virginia. The smaller of the two ships was *De Heylige Gheest* (*The Holy Ghost*); the larger had been rechristened the *Palatine*. Two ships of sad destiny! One for lack of a competent navigator; the other because it was sailed by a crew of hellions, the Devil's sweepings of the Seven Seas.

After prayers the Palatines, loaded with personal luggage, boarded their ships. Three hundred of them, mostly farmers and their families, crowded aboard the *Heylige Gheest* and began to search for some small space where they could rest and stow their luggage. This was nearly impossible. The vessel was already loaded below deck with casks of food and barrels of water, leaving little room for the passengers. Even the deck was crowded with hastily constructed pens for the cows, horses, sheep and swine which were to accompany the immigrants to the new world.

On board the *Palatine* conditions were somewhat better. She was a larger ship of about three hundred tons. Her passengers were mainly artisans and merchants, some of them moderately wealthy. Included on the passenger list was a titled German count, a former landgrave who had lost jurisdiction over his estates. He was accompanied by his daughter, a lovely lady of breeding. Most of these immigrants carried with them personal belongings of considerable value. Below deck were stored expensive furniture, tapestries, rich fabrics, books, a printing press and craft tools. There were also rare and exotic foods together with one hundred casks of vintage Rhenish wines.

At the turn of the tide, mooring lines were cast off, sails unfurled, and the two ships slowly sailed away toward the open sea. Past the Hook of Holland they stood and into the North Sea. That first evening, a brilliant sunset was obscured by black clouds. Then, in the dark watches of night, a mighty gale struck them with terrific fury. Great waves battered the vessels, hurling tons of water over their decks. Pens, animals and deck cargo were swept overboard. Sailors, braving death, climbed rain-slicked masts to secure the sails. Others worked without pause in a desperate battle to pump out the water which flowed into the strained hulls from opened seams. After a long eight hours, the storm abated.

The *Palatine*, one of her masts fractured by the storm, was forced to put in at an English port for repairs. The *Heylige Gheest* headed into the wind briefly while the bodies of five passengers who died during the storm were consigned to a watery grave. Afterward, she sailed toward America, her sails white wings of hope.

For the next twenty weeks, the little ship played blindman's buff over the broad reaches of the Atlantic, following a course set by wind, currents and a navigator who scarcely knew the points of the compass. Overcrowding and bad water took a toll of lives. Each morning the dead were collected and with brief ceremony thrown overboard. Food became contaminated and hunger stalked the decks. Storms belabored the ship. The master and navigator became ill and died, leaving the ship without effective leadership. Then fate played a cruel jest on the weakened survivors.

On January 3, 1739, the watch sighted land. The suffering Palatines crowded the top deck, laughing and crying with joy. More than half of the ship's company had died during the long voyage.

Sailing close to shore, the *Heylige Gheest* came to anchor off the Virginia Capes, and a party of thirty men set forth in search of food. They penetrated deep into the forest but met no one. They saw no game and recognized no plant of known nutritional value. When night came, they built a fire in a clearing and lay on the ground to sleep.

In the night a mass of frigid air crept over the land. Lethal cold touched the sleeping men with fingers of death. In the morning, only four of the hunting party awoke. The others lay about the ashes of their campfire, huddled in frozen silence.

Frantic with horror, the four survivors staggered back to the beach where they had left their boats. With trembling limbs they rowed to their ship. It was strangely silent. No watchman stood on the deck; no smoke wreathed the cooking galley. The four men boarded the *Heylige Gheest* to discover that the deadly cold air had visited the ship. It had become a floating coffin. In the stillness of the frigid night, all aboard had perished.

The *Palatine*, after repairs to her mast at Cowes, England, also set sail toward the new lands of promise. Like the *Heylige Gheest*, she also met with violent storms and adverse winds. Privation and disease decimated the ship's company. On

Christmas Day, three long months after the ship sailed from Cowes, a lookout sighted land. It proved to be the sandy shores of Cape Cod. The ship's officers and leaders of the Palatines held a council on the deck and decided to sail to Newport, where food and water supplies could be replenished.

As the battered vessel sailed within sight of the coast, a heavy snowstorm developed. The sailors on watch peered through the snow-shrouded gloom trying to sight some landmark by which they might shape their course. Below decks, the Palatines huddled together sharing the common misery as their ship drove south before a northeast wind.

On Block Island, cruel wreckers saw the riding lights of the immigrant vessel bobbing in the darkness. One of the wreckers tied a lantern on the back of a cow and led the creature across rocky highlands in sight of the sea. To the benumbed watch on the *Palatine*, the lantern appeared to be the riding light of a storm-tossed ship. When the swaying light was pointed out to the master of the *Palatine*, he ordered his helmsman to steer the ship in the wake of the stranger. At the fatal order, the helm was turned and the plunging vessel headed toward the rocky shores.

The *Palatine* struck the island with a crushing impact that tore a great hole in the hull. The tall masts snapped at deck level and fell, trapping many of the crew in a tangle of ropes, spars and sail. The wind seemed to pause as if aghast at the terrible destruction.

From the shore came triumphant shouts of the wreckers as they boarded their victim. Like a pack of bloodthirsty wolves they climbed over the wreckage. They were followers of the ancient adage that "dead men tell no tales." With sadistic efficiency they murdered everyone aboard the stricken ship. Everyone? No! One woman, the countess, hid in a rope locker. Through a crack in the door she watched the wreckers stab and kill her shipmates.

All through the night, the Block Island wreckers pillaged the *Palatine*. Furniture, rare fabrics, wines, the gold rings and jewels taken from the bodies of the slain immigrants were carried ashore. In the gray of dawn the murderers set the wreck on fire. Some quirk of wind or tide lifted the doomed *Palatine* from her rocky cradle, and she floated away from the shore while water poured into her wounded hull and flames leaped high over her deck.

The jubilant wreckers on the island's shore were suddenly stricken with awe and fear by the sound of shrill screams from the burning wreck. A woman, silhouetted by a background of flames, stood on the bow of the sinking ship, her arms rigidly pointing toward the shore. Her screams were stilled, to be succeeded by demented laughter. As the murderous wreckers watched, the bow of the *Palatine* lifted into the air and the ship slowly slid from sight beneath the waves.

Many times since that fateful night, sailors, yachtsmen and fishermen while approaching Block Island in the dark morning hours have claimed that they have seen in the distance a wildly burning wreck. Some of them are said to have heard the demented laughter of the countess.

Such is the legend of the wreck of the *Palatine*.

The true story of the wreck of the *Palatine* is every bit as fascinating as the famous legend.

Skippered by a rapacious master and manned by a crew of mutinous rascals, it was inevitable that trouble would develop on the voyage of the *Palatine*. The master mulcted the immigrants at every opportunity. He impounded their food and sold it back to them at exorbitant prices, charged them for every service and even used threats to obtain possession of their worldly goods. As the weeks passed, the strongbox in the master's cabin filled with gold. At last, retribution caught up with the rascal. When the coast of Massachusetts was sighted, the crew of the *Palatine* mutinied. They beat and robbed the ship's officers and terrorized the passengers. Casks of wine and spirits were broached, and the crew became drunk.

All discipline and decency, even the safety of the ship, were forgotten. The vessel was allowed to roll in the troughs of the sea with no one at the helm. Suddenly a savage northeast gale, bringing with it sleet and snow, staggered the *Palatine*, and it nearly foundered. Frightened sailors furled the sails, tied the helm and manned the pumps for a short time. However, they soon went back to their drinking. They swaggered below and tore Palatine wives and daughters from the arms of their husbands and families. Anyone who resisted was killed. Darkness did not halt the drunken orgy. Meanwhile the ship was being driven toward a rocky coast.

In the small hours of morning, the day after Christmas, the *Palatine* crashed on the rocky ledges of Block Island. Many of the sailors were killed or washed overboard to a watery grave. Yet a group of mutineers continued to control the ship, refusing to allow the Palatines on deck.

Two days after, a Block Islander, searching the rocky highlands for a lost sheep, sighted the wreck. It was still snowing and the cold wind was whipping spray over the shattered hulk.

Quickly a group of rescuers gathered on the rocks near the stricken ship. In the face of the pounding seas, at the peril of life and limb, the intrepid islanders boarded the *Palatine*. They were forced to subdue the mutinous seamen before rescue operations could begin.

The scene aboard the wreck was indescribable. Debris covered the deck. In the dark spaces below, the Palatines clung together in small groups, weeping and wailing, refusing to be rescued. The three days spent facing terror and death had temporarily unbalanced their minds.

One by one, the survivors were taken ashore and transported on horseback across drifted snow to the Simon Ray House, a large barnlike structure built by early settlers of the island.

Island women with blankets and warm food ministered to the needs of the unhappy people.

One hundred and five of the ship's company were rescued. Fifteen died later from exposure.

After all survivors were thought to have been rescued, an island man of color boarded the battered wreck for a final search. He was alone. The rest of the rescuers were on their way to the Ray House.

Hearing a faint cry for help, the islander hunted through the wreckage on deck but could find no one. Courageously he penetrated the Stygian darkness below deck. Groping his way, he came to a ladder which descended to the bilge where ballast was generally stored. Below, he could hear the swish of water as the seas entered the ship through her torn hull. He was about to leave when he heard a faint cry.

"Who is down there?" he shouted.

"Please—please save me," came a cry from below. "Don't leave me."

It was the voice of a woman. Cautiously the islander eased his weight on the ladder and slowly descended. His feet plunged into icy water. He hesitated in fear of the unknown. Then he heard a sob from below, and it filled him with pity and resolution. He descended the ladder until the water was touching his arms.

"Where are you?" he shouted.

The water swirled and a small hand grasped his coat. He reached down and his strong arms encircled a woman's waist. With her weight dragging on him, he slowly climbed the ladder. On the deck, in the grayness of the stormy day, he looked at the woman whom he had snatched from the watery grave. She was young and fair, and very nearly exhausted. He carried her to the bow and looked at the rocky shore. The wind had intensified and great waves were breaking around the bow of the wreck and hurling their weight viciously against the rocks.

A person struck by one of those waves would be crushed. The cold air, seeping through his wet clothing, was pricking his flesh with tiny slivers of pain. The girl in her light clothing must feel it more. The islander took off his coat, wrapped it around her and picked her up in his arms. Closely he watched the coursing waves. A large comber broke over the rocks and foamed angrily back toward the sea. The rescuer, holding his human burden close, jumped to the rocky shore, staggered, caught his balance and ran up the slope, racing a pursuing wave.

The islander took the girl to his home where, with the help of his mother, he nursed her back to health. During her convalescence, she often conversed with her rescuer, telling him of her childhood in the Palatinate. She told him of her father, the count, and of the old castle on the Rhine where she was born. Her father was gone. He had died in the wreck of the *Palatine*. She was now alone, friendless, in a strange land.

What her rescuer said to her may be left to the imagination. Suffice to say that several months later, a smiling blond German countess was united in wedlock to her benefactor, a colored Block Island fisherman.

The Palatinate was a large principality combining the authority of the counts palatine of Lorraine and Rhine. It had an unenviable history of conquest and ravishment by warring armies.

In 1689 the country was systematically devastated by a retreating French army. It was this destruction that led to the first wave of German overseas migration. Many of the early settlers of Pennsylvania came from the Palatinate.

Scandalous Affairs of a Baronet
and a Tavern Maid

Perhaps the most notorious love affair of colonial New England was the unconventional amour of Sir Charles Henry Frankland and Agnes Surriage, a tavern maid of Marblehead, Massachusetts. Their misadventures, eccentricities and shamelessly displayed passion for each other provided plenty of scandalous gossip for the loquacious purveyors of news in that period.

Sir Charles Henry, more familiarly known as Sir Harry, was an extremely wealthy baronet who had been sent to Boston in 1741 as collector of customs. He was a bachelor, young and handsome. Naturally such an eligible man was legitimate prey for a flock of ambitious mothers with marriageable daughters. He was wined and dined, invited to every social, political and sporting event in the colony and pursued more or less openly by a bevy of matrimony-minded females. It was a great life. Blissfully basking in this aureole of public approbation, Sir Harry was happy and contented until the day he literally fell for a bewitching young girl named Agnes Surriage. It happened in this manner.

In the summer of 1742 Sir Harry's official duties sent him riding to Marblehead, where he was to inspect the fortifications of Fort Sewall that were being built to defend the harbor. The day was hot, and the baronet stopped at the Fountain Inn for a draught of cooling ale. As he entered the taproom, his feet slipped on a wet, soapy spot on the floor. Ungracefully he fell, landing with a thud on the seat of his fashionable trousers. When he was able to focus his eyes, he found himself gazing at such a vision of lovely young womanhood that for a moment he wondered if his fall had upended him into paradise.

She had long black hair which mantled her shapely shoulders, and a pair of mischievous blue eyes shaded by long curved eyelashes. Her features were delicately tinted with the rose of perfect health. Her lips were full and red—and expressive. Even the shapeless skirt she wore failed to conceal the perfect symmetry of her lower limbs, while the swelling glories of her flowering maturity were partly revealed by a low neckline.

She had been scrubbing the floor. Now, one hand still holding a dripping brush, she looked at the fallen baronet in seemly consternation, although a glint of amusement sparkled in her eyes.

Sir Harry had spent his formative years in the reckless, amoral atmosphere of the English court, where every man hunted pleasure and every woman was a possible victim of his desires. Even though still a young man in years, he had once possessed a mistress and owned himself the sire of an illegitimate son. He was a master of the gay, pointed inconsequential small talk of the drawing room.

"Ah, my beautiful queen, you have brought me to my knees," he remarked whimsically.

"Faith, is that what you sit upon?" she asked slyly.

He laughed, pleased by her humor and quick repartee. His bold glances wandered from her bare feet to her shapely ankles and legs.

"Are you the innkeeper's daughter?" he inquired.

"Lawdy me! No!" she answered. "I'm the daughter of a

farmer. My name, please your honor, is Agnes Surriage. I work here in the inn as a maid and cleaning girl."

Frankland touched her bare foot. "Such lovely members should be clothed in gold. Here is a crown. Take it and buy yourself the finest shoes in Marblehead."

Shyly the girl accepted the gold coin, smiling her thanks. "My Lord, you are a generous and kindly man. I must say thee good-by now, for I have my work to do."

Sir Harry hesitated, hoping to prolong their meeting, but Agnes was already at work scrubbing the wet floor. Reluctantly he left her.

The devastating effect this sixteen-year-old girl had on Sir Harry Frankland was astounding. He returned to Boston in a daze. Suddenly he discovered that life had lost its savor. The usually interesting rounds of social engagements he found boring. He pursued and dallied with several Boston beauties, but they could not erase the memory of Agnes Surriage from his mind.

In a short time, Sir Harry again found official business which required his presence in Marblehead. Forthwith he set out for that town, without tarrying on the way.

When the young man arrived at the Fountain Inn, his early training among the young rakes of the London court asserted itself. He engaged the most pretentious room in the inn. Then, after crossing the fellow's palm with gold, he requested the innkeeper to send Agnes to his room. He had little time to compose himself before the girl, after a timid knock, entered the room.

"You sent for me?" she asked, smiling shyly at him.

Again he was stricken by her fresh young beauty. Whatever his intentions may have been, he was completely disarmed by her presence. Like a callow schoolboy on his first date, he stammered and found himself at a loss for words. He glanced at her bare feet.

"You are not wearing shoes," he blurted.

"I bought shoes—lovely shoes—too pretty to wear while I work. I wear them when I go to church. Wait but a moment and I will show them to you."

As she turned to leave the room, Sir Harry swept her into his arms and kissed her. She submitted meekly for a moment, then looked up at him gravely. "Do you dally with me because I am naught but a servant?" she asked him.

"No!" he protested vehemently. "In my eyes you are a lady—a beautiful, adorable lady."

She shook her head with a sad smile, pointing to her skirt and bare legs. "Would a lady dress like this? Would a lady be seen without shoes?"

A bizarre idea flashed in his mind. "I shall make you a lady," he said, shutting his eyes to all obstacles. "Come with me to Boston. I will send you to school, buy you the prettiest gowns. Someday I will present you to the governor and his lady."

"Why would you do all these things for me?" she asked, her eyes shining at the vision his promises had conjured.

"Because I love you," he answered. Again he kissed her and was surprised to see tears in her eyes.

"If you wish me to be a lady, you should treat me as such," she cautioned him.

Sir Harry groaned but conceded her the point. "Inform your parents that I will call upon them."

Agnes kissed his hand and hurried from the room.

The following day, Sir Harry Frankland visited the humble Surriage cottage and broached his proposal to Agnes's parents. At first they demurred, but the baronet persuaded them that his interest in their daughter was merely altruistic. All he wished to do was to give Agnes the finer things in life. Eventually the Surriages agreed.

Sir Harry returned to Boston and made arrangements for his young protégé to attend a fashionable school run by Peter

Pelham, a most respectable schoolmaster. He also engaged the Reverend Dr. Edward Holyoke, President of Harvard College, to give her religious instruction. A comfortable room in a Boston inn was secured for the girl. Soon after, she arrived in Boston accompanied by her mother.

Agnes and her mother were hardly settled before Sir Harry took the girl on a shopping tour of the city. Shoes, dresses and gowns with all the accoutrement of fashion were purchased. Her wardrobe soon rivaled that possessed by the governor's lady.

Agnes enjoyed the experience of attending Mr. Pelham's distinguished school. Her schoolmates were the daughters of Boston's wealthier families. After school hours, Sir Harry often took her for rides in his gold and red chaise. There was no one to say no. Mrs. Surriage, worried over her sick husband, had returned to Marblehead.

It was inevitable that the beautiful young girl would fall in love with her charming benefactor. Shortly before Christmas, Sir Harry invited Agnes to visit his home in Cambridge. The house with its rich furnishings delighted her. The servants, captivated by her beauty and graciousness, vied to serve her, and the baronet was at his charming best. It was enough to turn the head of any girl.

After a carefree dinner by candlelight, Sir Harry evinced no disposition to escort her back to her inn. Instead, he passionately declared his love for her but carefully explained that an English baronet could not marry a girl of low degree. Apparently Agnes loved her Sir Harry so much that she was willing to forego the formality of wedlock. That night she did not return to the inn. The following morning, a carter arrived at that establishment and carried all of Agnes's possessions to the Frankland residence.

It was not long before the citizens of Boston became aware of this shocking, licentious affair. Agnes Surriage was sharing the bed and board of Sir Harry Frankland without any apparent scruples.

In 1742 there were plenty of Puritans living in the Bay Colony. The common people—tradesmen, artisans, farmers and laborers—were shocked and outraged by what was going on. Peter Pelham, the schoolmaster, suddenly discovered that he no longer had room in his school for Agnes. The Reverend Dr. Holyoke, after being informed of the sinful liaison, rode posthaste to the Frankland mansion and confronted the erring couple. Whatever he said to them did not alter the situation. The lovers refused to be discreet. On horseback or riding in a chaise, the two often visited the stores in Boston, greeting acquaintances with genial salutations, completely disregarding polite conventions. Public opinion ostracized them. People of consequence turned their backs on the pair, and some of the shopkeepers began to show a marked reluctance to serve them.

Angered by the narrowness of the Bostonians, Sir Harry bought a large tract of land in Hopkinton. Hiring the best artisans available, he had them construct a magnificent mansion for his Agnes. Erected on the side of a hill, the house commanded a splendid vista of rolling farmlands and hardwood forests not yet laid low by the settlers' axes. A spacious hall, sustained by Ionic columns, was hung with rich tapestries from England. In the parlor a great fireplace, the mantel and facings made of Italian marble, occupied an entire wall. French wallpaper with paneled scenes from Greek mythology gave gay color to the room. The grounds surrounding the house were terraced, planted with rare trees and shrubbery and watered from a large spring.

In this setting the lovers lived in apparent bliss, attended by twelve servants and a number of slaves. Frankland frequently invited some of the gayer young blades of the colony to visit his new estate, entertaining them with fox hunting and drinking bouts. Local hunters brought wild game to the mansion, and the baronet's cook served banquets which were without equal in New England.

For three happy years, Agnes and her Sir Harry lived and loved merrily in their Hopkinton retreat. During the first year, Agnes's father died. Sir Harry, perhaps as a sop to his conscience, gave Mrs. Surriage a large sum of money for some worthless land which she owned. He also sent to England for his bastard son, who joined the couple in Hopkinton.

Then, rather rashly, Sir Harry decided to take his Agnes to England, counting on her beauty and charm to open all doors. The pair sailed from Boston after a banquet and party in a local tavern which became the subject of several sermons the following Sabbath.

When the couple arrived in England, Sir Harry's family refused to meet him while he was accompanied by Agnes. They intimated that it was normal and proper to support a mistress, but one should not be indiscreet. It was most improper to display any passion for such a creature in public, and it was positively unheard of to present her to relatives and friends. Discomfitted by their reception, Sir Harry and Agnes shook the English dust from their feet and sailed to the Continent for a tour of Europe.

They traveled through France and Holland, where they secured a luxurious barge and enjoyed a leisurely trip down the romantic Rhine. They sampled the climate in Italy, Corsica and Spain. One evening, they arrived in Lisbon, Portugal, and hired a room in a famous hotel. The day had been unseasonably warm. After partaking of iced desserts, they retired to their room. In the night a terrific earthquake devastated the city. The hotel was demolished, burying Agnes and Sir Harry in the rubble. The girl was caught behind a slanting mass of masonry. By some miracle she was unhurt. Digging frantically with her hands, she finally freed herself and began a desperate search for her beloved. She found him pinned down by several beams, his body almost buried in the debris. He was badly injured. Through the night Agnes worked to release him. By superhuman effort she removed the beams and bricks from his body and dragged him to the street.

There were no medicine, no water and little food in Lisbon following the disaster. Somehow Agnes secured a room in a battered hovel and had her lover removed there. For three long months she nursed him as he hovered on the brink of no return. Love and constant care defeated death. Slowly the baronet began to improve. Agnes's courage and devotion overcame the inherent snobbishness bred into him. When he was able to walk, the couple visited a magistrate and were legally married.

With some trepidation, the newlyweds returned to England. But the story of Agnes's rescue of Sir Harry had preceded them. She had become a heroine, and their love had publicly ascended from the moral depths to a classic story of devotion. Thus Sir Harry's relatives and friends welcomed the pair with open arms.

Some time later, Agnes and her husband returned to Boston where Lady Agnes Frankland was met and welcomed by the governor's lady. Bostonians who had once ostracized them were eager to be seen in their company. The couple returned to their mansion in Hopkinton where they lived together happily until the death of the baronet a few years later.

The love story of Agnes Surriage and Sir Harry Frankland has always been a favorite. Their romance took place during what might be called the Golden Era. It was a brief period between wars. Prosperity in New England was evident. The Port of Boston was crowded with ships, some bringing to the colonies the luxuries and refinements of Europe, others, laden with New England products, sailing to foreign lands. The early Puritan opposition to ostentatiousness in dress and the display of wealth had disappeared to a great extent. Architects, skilled woodworkers, the builders of fine furniture, even portrait painters, were busy catering to the demands for lovely and well-furnished homes. European artisans were migrating to Boston to set up shops and factories and to share in the general prosperity.

However, the bubble burst all too soon. In 1745 another war with the French was in progress. The depredations of French privateers and a costly New England expedition which resulted in the conquest of Louisburg brought a sharp curtailment of spending. Land values dropped and it was several years before prosperity returned.

Hearts and Pirates

Samuel Cranston stole stealthily past the drunken watchman, crouching low so that his silhouette would not show above the gunwale. It was a black night but a keen-eyed man could have seen him. A dozen pirates were frolicking with a group of captive Indian women in the waist of the ship. If they discovered him attempting an escape, he would die quickly.

He reached the stern of the ship and risked a glance over the taffrail. Below he could faintly see the dark outline of the jolly boat. Beneath her seat he had secreted a box of ship biscuits and a jug of fresh water. It was not much but it would have to do.

Throwing a rope over the side, he tied the end to a ringbolt in the deck and lowered himself over the rail. Holding on to the rope, he felt around until his bare feet touched the small craft. Next moment, he was aboard. Setting her adrift he sat hunched on the seat, listening for any sound of alarm. The dull gleam of the hooded anchor light on the pirate vessel faded. He picked up the oars and began to row.

The sun, creeping over the horizon, found him still rowing. He had been rowing without pause for five hours. Finally he ceased his labor and stood up, looking intently in all directions.

There was no sign of land or ship. He had made his escape. Lying down in the cramped bottom of the boat, he slept.

The next few days he experienced all the dread sufferings which are the lot of castaways on the bosom of the ocean. Taking bearings from the sun, he rowed several hours each day, always heading westward. His muscles ached from the strain, and his hands grew puffy and raw from salt water sores occasioned by ruptured blisters. His greatest hell was the mental anguish suffered as he thought of the many good things of life that he had been deprived of by a recalcitrant fate.

Most often, he thought of Mary his wife, as he had done so many times in the seven years of his captivity. He visualized the soft beauty of her face, the clean, sweet texture of her skin, her brown, naturally wavy hair, the tiny upthrust of the tip of her dainty nose, the full red lips which unsuccessfully tried to conceal lovely white teeth. He dreamed of the intimacies they had shared and of the many daily, homely events which make up a happy household. He thought of his house, the "Castle," a noteworthy mansion on Thames Street in Newport, Rhode Island.

Now, seven years later, Samuel Cranston was puzzled to understand the urge which had induced him to leave all that was near and dear to him and go away on a hazardous voyage. Inwardly he realized that it had been caused by a hope of personal gain. The loss of several ships in which he had invested money had depleted his fortune. He had hoped to recoup the losses quickly. So he had tempted fate.

It had been a beautiful day when he boarded the *Ranger*, bound for Jamaica. On the dock the women who had come to wish them Godspeed waved as the ship gained headway and moved slowly toward the harbor mouth. He had stood by the rail, his eyes glued on his wife Mary until the ship tacked and he lost sight of the wharf.

A steady northwest wind had winged them swiftly down

the coast. They spoke no other ship, but many times the lookouts shouted "Sail ho!" Far on the horizon, a tiny patch of white would be seen, wings of commerce on the broad avenues of the sea.

Ten days out, after a fast voyage, they rounded the tip of Florida and sailed to the west in sight of the Florida Keys. The captain had invited the three passengers and Cranston to the cabin for a drink of rum.

"We are now off the Florida Keys, and only ten days out of Newport," he told them. "Here! Drink a toast to a quick voyage to Kingston Harbor."

The voyage had ended quickly. But the passengers and crew of the *Ranger* never looked upon Kingston Harbor.

The wind which had been so favorable to the Newport brig died to a series of intermittent light breezes. The sails would fill for a short time, and then, as if weary, would sag and hang lifeless from the yardarms. That night at dusk, the lookout high on the mainmast sighted a sail a short distance to the south. It appeared to be a large sloop.

During the night the *Ranger* made little progress. Early in the morning the strange sloop was only a mile away. Some freak breeze was sending her swiftly toward the brig. The captain had communicated to Samuel Cranston his belief that the stranger was a pirate craft. Guns were run out and the crew made ready for a vigorous defense. Hoisting a black flag, the stranger bore down on the hapless brig.

The defense of the Newporters against the pirates was pitifully weak. Their two starboard four-pounders fired grapeshot at the advancing ship without noticeable results. The sloop sailed alongside the *Ranger*, and a dozen grappling irons were thrown aboard. The two ships bumped together. Instantly a wild crew of pirates leaped on the deck and with bloodthirsty cries attacked the Newporters. The crew of the *Ranger* fought fiercely with pike and sword, but they were outnumbered five to one. They died fighting on the deck of their ship. The passengers were murdered in their cabins. Only one man was left alive, Samuel Cranston. Why? Perhaps the pirates were temporarily sated with killing.

Whatever the reason, he had been disarmed and kicked aboard the pirate ship to become a slave to the whole hellish crew, an errand boy forever on call to fetch and carry, rewarded with curses and cuffs, until his escape.

Samuel Cranston stood up in the jolly boat and searched the sea for a sail. His water and food were nearly depleted. Five days after he left the pirate ship he was sighted by an English vessel and taken aboard. She was the *Betsy Howland*, bound for Nova Scotia.

Mary Hart Cranston had been bitterly disappointed by her husband's decision to sail to Jamaica. He intended to select an agent to represent him in that country and to sell future cargoes of horses and other Rhode Island exports. She could not understand why he did not send someone else to hire an agent. However, as a good wife, she had made no objections but had helped in every way to make his voyage comfortable. Her solicitude for his well-being doubled the size of the baggage he had planned to take. She had showered him with loving attentions. She had tried to be cheerful the night before the *Ranger* sailed, but when he had taken her into his arms, her composure had crumpled. She cried, stricken by the imminence of his departure. The following morning she had smiled and waved with other wives and sweethearts as the smart little brig caught the breeze and sailed out of the harbor. Then she had cried again. For weeks a heavy knot seemed to be lodged in her breast.

The waiting was hard. Two months went by and she began to make daily trips to the docks, trying to glean some information concerning the whereabouts of the *Ranger*. It should arrive home soon.

Several more weeks passed, and she tried to fight a dark feeling of fear that she would never again look upon her husband's face. As months went by, the fear in her heart crystallized into certainty. Her husband, kind, handsome Samuel Cranston, must be dead.

It was two years later when the first information concerning the disappearance of the *Ranger* was received in Newport. A small brig manned by a pirate crew had been captured off Barbados and taken into the Port of Providence. It was identified as the missing *Ranger*. One of the crew, before he was publicly hanged, confessed to the authorities that every man aboard the ship had been murdered on the morning she had been seized by the pirates near the Florida Keys.

Mary Cranston accepted the certainty that her husband was dead. She was a widow and she was young. A pretty widow with considerable property was an enticement to many bachelors. They wished to court her, but Mary refused for a long time to attend any social affairs.

One day, while visiting her brother-in-law's home, she was introduced to a Mr. Russell, a young merchant from Boston. He was handsome, of good deportment and well educated. Attracted by the charming widow, the young man found several opportunities to see and talk with her. He became a frequent visitor at the Castle, and Mary allowed him occasionally to escort her to some of the social events in Newport. Inevitably they fell in love, and she consented to become his wife. They decided to hold the wedding in Newport.

When the forthcoming wedding was announced, the couple received felicitations from the members of the Cranston family as well as from their many friends.

What were Mary Cranston's secret thoughts in the seclusion of her bedchamber as she prepared to welcome a second man into the intimacies of a wedded life. Had she forgotten Samuel, or was his memory a sad, sweet page of love locked in her heart? Perhaps, sometimes of a night, she might have dreamed of him. In the daytime, however, she found no time for dreaming. There were so many details to be taken care of and the days were not long enough.

The wedding day arrived, one of those rare days when earth and sky seemed to be in tune. In the Castle, servants were preparing a wedding feast. Outside, on the spacious lawn, wedding guests were gathering. The minister who would perform the ceremony was refreshing himself in the pantry. Mary Cranston, with the assistance of a flustered slave girl, was putting the finishing touches to her toilet. Suddenly a female servant entered the bedroom, nervously twisting her fingers together.

"Madam!" she said. "There is a man in the kitchen who wishes to speak to you."

Tense and excited, Mary Cranston spoke sharply. "Do not bother me. Can you not see that I am busy. Tell the man to leave at once."

The servant, her eyes big with excitement, hesitated, took a few steps toward the door and halted, to speak in a voice that was close to a whisper.

"Madam, this man said that he must see you. He told me to tell you that he saw your husband, Samuel Cranston, this morning at the ferry."

The shadows of late afternoon were creeping behind buildings and trees as a sloop sailed into Boston Harbor and tied up at Long Wharf. A sturdy, sad-faced man thanked the captain and stepped ashore. He carried no baggage. The clothes he wore were clean but shabby. With a purposeful step, he walked ashore and onto King Street.

The proprietor was making ready to close the doors as he entered the countinghouse of Francis Burrows. Master Burrows looked at the stranger's threadbare clothing.

"What can I do for you?" he asked.

"My name is Samuel Cranston of Newport. I have been away for seven years. Do you still handle my accounts here in Boston?"

"Glory be!" Burrows exclaimed with some asperity. "Do ye take me for a fool? Samuel Cranston is dead—killed by pirates. His widow is marrying Mr. Russell tomorrow."

Cranston grasped Burrows by the arm, his face registering shocked dismay. "Say ye again," he demanded.

"Mrs. Cranston is marrying Mr. Russell, a worthy young man of this town, tomorrow noon in Newport."

"No! It shall not be! I must stop it," Cranston said. "Ye must believe me. I *am* Samuel Cranston. I was captured by pirates. I escaped. I must get to Newport in time to stop the wedding. Listen! I can prove that I am Samuel Cranston. Did I not correspond with you seven years ago concerning the sale of a sloop? Do you not remember the sloop *Portsmouth Lady?*"

It was dark when Samuel Cranston, mounted on a horse provided by Master Burrows, started on the long ride to Newport. Three times during the night he stopped to rest his steed. The sun was shining in the east when he reached Bristol Ferry. Luckily the ferryboat was moored on the Bristol side of the bay. A friendly wind filled the big square sail. Yet the sun was high when the blunt-bowed craft arrived at the Portsmouth shore.

A group of fashionably dressed wedding guests, gathered in front of the Castle, paid little attention to the worn-looking man on the jaded horse who rode past them toward the stables. No one noticed him dismount and enter the kitchen door.

A maid, turning a spit before the fireplace, saw him and hurried to bar his way.

"What are ye doing here?" she demanded. "Go away!"

The stranger did not seem disturbed by her hostility. Instead he spoke to her commandingly. "Tell your mistress that I would speak with her. I have a message."

Stubbornly the maid shook her head. "She cannot be disturbed. She is making ready for her wedding."

"I must see her now. Tell her that her husband Samuel was seen this morning on the Bristol Ferry."

The servant's eyes opened wide at this momentous news. Turning, she ran from the room.

Samuel Cranston waited in the kitchen, wondering how his wife would react when she received the message from the maid. Would she consent to see him? What would he say to her?

There was the sound of a step on the threshold, and Mary, her face white with shock, walked into the room. She was dressed in her wedding gown, her hair carefully coiffured. She was beautiful. Samuel fought a fierce impulse to take her in his arms.

"You—you told my servant that you have news of—of my husband," she said, her eyes searching his face without recognizing him.

Samuel nodded. He pushed the hair back from his forehead, revealing a crescent-shaped scar. "Do you remember this scar, Mary? Do you not know me?"

His wife gave a stifled scream and fell forward into his arms. It might have been a cry of either joy or—anguish.

"Fetch a cloth and wet it with cold water," he commanded the servant girl. "Your mistress has swooned."

Mary Cranston soon recovered. Within a short time Mr. Russell and the wedding guests were told of the extraordinary return from the dead of Samuel Cranston.

The shock to Mr. Russell was severe, yet he was able to hide his feelings from the assemblage.

"It is only fitting that a wedding take place," he said to Samuel. "The position of groom is yours. I would like permission to give away the bride."

Later that day Mary and Samuel Cranston stood before the gathering and renewed their wedding vows. Samuel, shaved and dressed in his best, was said by some of the ladies present to be even more handsome than he had been on his first wedding day. Russell returned to Boston but always remained friendly with the Cranstons.

Samuel Cranston had the distinction of serving as governor of Rhode Island for a period of twenty-nine years. He died in office on April 26, 1727. His charming and talented wife was the granddaughter of Roger Williams.

The Strange Battle of Windham

Perhaps the Devil did have a hand, as was often remarked later, in the strange occurrence which terrorized the village of Windham in Connecticut on a dark night in June, 1754.

It had been a year of fear and foreboding for the inhabitants of the village. In March, deep snows followed by torrential rains had flooded fields, dampened houses and barns, causing precious supplies of food to become moldy. Then a traveling clergyman who preached a sermon in the meetinghouse had frightened and depressed the Windhamites by labeling them as unrepentant sinners and forecasting that a wrathful God would shower down on them a series of calamities. In April a bloody axe was found on the village green. A few days later, a supposedly friendly Indian struck Squire Elderkin and threatened to have Windham burned to the ground by his friends, the powerful and savage Susquehanna Indians of New York and Pennsylvania. All these portents were followed by weeks of severe drought, engendering a feeling of apprehension in the breasts of the God-fearing inhabitants.

On the night of June 17 terror struck Windham. On that night Goodman White's Negro slave Pomp paid a visit to his dusky sweetheart Phyllis, who lived in a farmhouse some distance from the village. Enchanted by his charming girl friend,

Pomp stayed far later than was his wont. When he left the farmhouse it was very late, and the night was darker than a hat. To bolster his courage, he fingered a Voodoo charm and whistled a hymn. These measures seemed effective against ghosts and their ilk, for he reached the village green without mishap. He paused in front of the meetinghouse, his safety assured by the surrounding houses.

Suddenly an uproar of sound shattered the silence of the night. Roars, bellows, shrieks—a cacaphony of ear-splitting noise enveloped the village, seemingly coming from every quarter. Pomp fled, his frightened cries adding to the uproar.

The clamor awoke every inhabitant in the village. Dogs barked, babies cried and excited people shouted. The men grabbed their muskets and powder horns and assembled on the green, ready to fight for their lives while the women and children huddled behind barred doors. Most of the villagers were sure that the dreaded Susquehanna Indians had surrounded Windham and were preparing to attack. Every moment the brave defenders expected to see shadowy forms, armed with tomahawks and knives, advancing toward them.

The noise continued but no Indian warriors appeared. Their nerves on edge, the little group of armed men crouching on the green thought they heard distinct articulations amid the general uproar. Voices from the darkness were calling for the surrender of Squire Elderkin and Colonel Dyer, two of the village's most distinguished citizens.

One of the nervous defenders voiced his opinion that the two gentlemen should surrender themselves to the savages, thus averting a general massacre of their neighbors. Squire Elderkin then suggested in a trembling voice that Colonel Dyer, being a younger man, should be the first to give himself up to the Indians. Perhaps one man would satisfy them. Colonel Dyer, however, was more interested in staying alive than he was in sacrificing himself for his neighbors. Angrily he retorted that perhaps the savages would be satisfied with an old moose like the Squire.

All through the remainder of the night, the Windhamites huddled on the village green, listening to the hellish hubbub. Gradually, the noise subsided. Silence finally descended on the neighborhood as the first rays of the morning sun tinted the sky.

From dawn till noon the Windham defenders stayed on guard, but no enemies made their appearance. Scouts were sent out to search the surrounding woodlands. No Indians or any signs of Indians were found. However, the scouts did find thousands of dead frogs lying in the hardened mud of dried-up marshes. Such a sight had never been seen before.

After a period of cogitation the people of Windham came to the conclusion that the horrible uproar which had frightened them so badly was caused by these thousands of frogs engaged in a savage battle of death for the few puddles of moisture left in the dry swamps.

The voices which called for the surrender of Squire Elderkin and Colonel Dyer must have been nothing more than the wrought-up imagination of the Windham defenders. This was probably not the first time that a case of mass hysteria affected an entire settlement in colonial days.

Governor Wentworth's Search
for a Wife

Vivacious, beautiful Molly Pittman, with the natural grace of a healthy young girl, walked with swinging strides along Sagamore Road toward her home. It was a lovely day, a day to enjoy. She sang snatches of folk songs in a sweet contralto voice as her soft leather boots kicked up tiny spurts of dust from the road. A tote bag of corn meal bobbed over one shoulder, but she scarcely felt its weight. She had much to remember—and dream about.

In Portsmouth she had seen young Richard Shortridge, an apprentice of Noah Calk the wheelwright. The lad had dashed into the street as she was passing the carriage shop and stood in front of her so that she was forced to tarry. She had met the young man several times by chance but never in this manner. He had gazed at her silently, his lively brown eyes sending a message which pinked her cheeks and sent delightful shivers rippling over her body.

"I will call on you this evening," he blurted. Then his face flushed, and he had stammered, "if—if—ye w-will allow me."

She had smiled and nodded her head, her heart pounding so loudly that she feared he might hear it. At that moment Noah Calk had bawled for him from the shop. With a sudden fierce intensity Richard caught her hand in a strong grip. Awkwardly he bent over and brushed his warm lips across her fingers. Then he turned and ran back to the shop. Aye! She had plenty to think upon—and dream about.

A clatter of horse's hoofs and the rattle of a carriage on the rough dirt road shattered her dreams. Stepping to the side of the road she faced toward the disturbance to see a silver and gold coach approaching, drawn by four white horses. A plump coachman handled the reins and two slim footmen bobbed in back. The trio were dressed in brilliant red livery. Astride lively black mounts were two outriders, also in livery. It was the magnificent equipage of the royal governor of New Hampshire, Benning Wentworth, traveling to his estate at Little Harbor.

The girl looked with keen interest at these outward signs of extreme wealth. It was said that the governor received a salary of fourteen hundred pounds per annum in addition to the rents from vast land holdings. Yet Molly felt a small stir of pity for the great man—so wealthy but for what gain. His two sons had died in childhood. His wife, the pretty, spirited Lady Abigail, had died of a flux several years ago. Now he was alone, a master of pomp and ceremony, riding in his glittering carriage to the big house at Little Harbor, a house which held neither kith nor kin, only servants and slaves.

The coach drew abreast of Molly. Like a jack-in-the-box, the governor's face appeared at the carriage window. He stared at the girl and suddenly shouted a command to halt. The coachman pulled back on the reins and the conveyance rolled to a stop. Governor Benning Wentworth, resplendent in gold-lace-trimmed coat, embroidered waistcoat, white silk stockings and gold buckled shoes, stepped from his coach and bowed low to Molly.

"My dear!" he voiced. "Methink it's been ages since I have had the pleasure to feast mine eyes on such a charming young beauty. Pray tell me your name and where you live?"

Flattered by this attention from the great man, the girl smiled and curtsied.

"Please, Your Excellency, I am Molly Pittman. I live in my father's house at Pittman farm."

Benning Wentworth, captivated by the girl's fresh beauty, ogled her for a moment. "I must get acquainted with my neighbors. Tell your father that I will visit him anon," he said.

Again the governor bowed to her before re-entering his coach. A snap of the coachman's whip and the vehicle continued on its way. Molly watched the receding carriage until it turned into the Little Harbor Road.

That evening Richard Shortridge arrived at the Pittman farm to court Molly. Shy and bold in turn, his winsome manners and sturdy manliness captured the girl's heart. When the time arrived for the youth to return to Portsmouth, Molly, in adorable confusion, invited him to come again. Thereafter young Richard was taking the long walk to the Pittman farm almost every evening. However, the youth was soon opposed in his suit for Molly's hand by a redoubtable rival.

A fortnight after the girl's trip to Portsmouth, the ornate coach of Governor Wentworth halted in front of the Pittman farmhouse. The royal governor presented a gallant figure as he descended from his carriage. Although past his fifty-ninth birthday, he was a fine-looking man. Tall and broad-shouldered, of commanding appearance, he was gifted with a ready tongue and possessed the courtliness of a cavalier.

When the somewhat flustered Hosea Pittman confronted him at the door, Wentworth bowed and addressed the farmer without preliminaries.

"Sir! Although we have never met to my knowledge, you must know of me, for we have been neighbors for many years. I am Benning Wentworth of Little Harbor, governor of New Hampshire."

"Welcome!" said the farmer. "Please enter and tell me how I can serve thee."

The governor mentally contrasted the worn but serviceable furnishings in the farmhouse with the fine imported furniture of his own mansion at Little Harbor.

"As you may have heard," Wentworth said after being seated, "I am a widower without child. I have recently added a wing to my house at Little Harbor. A sixteen-room home requires supervision—by a woman. I am not young but I have the means to give a woman all that is needed for well-being and happiness. Sir, I have met your daughter. She appears pleasant and amenable. I believe she could make me an excellent wife. I have come here to ask permission to court Molly."

"Your Excellency!" Pittman answered. "Molly is young—and she is my only child. My one wish is for her happiness. She is being courted at present by an apprentice, a young man named Richard Shortridge of Portsmouth. I know not how much longer he will be in service, and I have heard of no understanding between him and Molly. Therefore I grant your request. Understand—I shall not try to influence her in your favor. The girl must make her own choice."

Several days later, Governor Wentworth invited Molly to a soiree at the great house. Here she was introduced to the most wealthy and prominent people in the province. The governor was a model of gallantry, showing himself attentive to the girl's every wish. She danced in the beautiful new stateroom and dined on delicacies from Europe and the West Indies.

However, something took place that evening at Little Harbor. Perhaps the governor became overbold or possibly Molly heard some of the whispered stories of "affairs" between Wentworth and his female servants. Whatever the reason, the girl returned home at an early hour, vowing never to speak to the governor again.

Richard Shortridge continued to call at the Pittman home, and his master, Noah Calk, the wheelwright, let it be known that his apprentice would soon finish his term of service and planned to marry pretty Molly Pittman.

Without question, Governor Wentworth must have heard this bit of gossip. To a man so proud of wealth and position, this must have been a shocking blow—to have a farmer's poppet reject him in favor of a miserable apprentice. He must have entertained vengeful thoughts.

One day a British man-o'-war from the West Indies anchored in Portsmouth Harbor, and the King's officers were pleased to accept an invitation to a dinner at the governor's mansion at Little Harbor.

It was a splendid affair. The stateroom, lit by dozens of candles, was filled with ladies dressed in lovely satin and brocaded dresses, their hair embellished with high wigs, and gentlemen dressed in tight satin knee pants and colored waistcoats trimmed with snowy Flemish lace. The colorful uniforms of the British officers added brilliance to the assembly.

After an elaborate dinner, the governor invited the captain of the warship to his study where they could converse privately over brandy and sweetmeats served by slaves.

"My ship is dangerously undermanned," the captain told Wentworth. "A distemper suffered in the Bahamas killed many of my men. I beg leave to impress a few able-bodied men in the streets of Portsmouth after dark."

Benning Wentworth leaned across the table, a wicked smile on his face. "I know where you might pick up one man this very night. A young man will soon be walking on Sagamore Road toward Portsmouth. If he was intercepted and taken aboard your ship, I would not be too unhappy."

The captain arose and bowed. "I will take care of that matter at once."

The following day, a British man-o'-war left Portsmouth

for England—and Noah Calk, the wheelwright, raised a hue and cry for a missing apprentice. Yet no one saw any connection between the departure of the English frigate and the disappearance of Richard Shortridge.

Canny Governor Wentworth waited a month before calling at the Pittman home. He was an old campaigner. With his rival out of the way, he believed that in time he would be able to induce Molly to become his wife. He pressed her to accept small gifts, placed his carriages at her service, escorted her to social gatherings and was ever flaunting his wealth before her eyes.

As the months drifted by without any word concerning Richard Shortridge, Molly fell more and more under the sway of the crafty governor. Between her deep love for Richard and her growing fondness for Benning Wentworth, she felt torn in twain. Finally, in desperation, the girl visited Old Mary Carew, who was said to be a witch.

"Mother Carew, I have come to ask ye a question that means much to me," she said to the old woman. "Can ye tell me what happened to Richard Shortridge?"

The witch dropped a handful of twigs on a black cloth and studied them intently. After many minutes she looked up at Molly.

"Owee! I have sad news for you, my pet. Richard Shortridge is dead."

Young Richard Shortridge, pressed aboard a British frigate, stripped of all he possessed, separated from his lovely Molly, sank to the depths of despair. He had been forced into the English Navy, a service where insults and blows were the accepted lot of all sailors. He received no sympathy from officers or his fellow shipmates. Like an animal or slave, he was forced to toil with no expectations of reward, only punishment for shortcomings or infractions of a multitude of rules. Somehow he survived.

He arrived in Plymouth, England, and was immediately transferred to another ship bound for the West Indies. Seven weeks later, his ship anchored in the harbor of New Providence in the Bahamas. For the first time since his impressment, Richard was allowed to go ashore. He saw several ships at anchor in the long reaches of the harbor. One of them was flying a Massachusetts ensign. Young Shortridge determined that he would board the New England ship and ask for assistance. Waiting until dark, he crept to the shore. After a desperate search he found a small boat tied to a jetty. The lights of the New England vessel twinkled in the distance. Richard jumped aboard the small boat and rowed out into the harbor.

When the shore party from the frigate congregated on the docks, one seaman was missing, the young American Richard Shortridge. Marines were sent through the town to search for him. If found, he would suffer thirty-five lashes on his back with the cat-o'-nine-tails, a punishment which usually killed the victim.

Late that night the deck watch on the brig *Boston Hope* was alerted by the sound of oars. They reached the rail in time to catch a man climbing aboard. Members of the watch overpowered him, bound his hands and took him to the captain.

After her visit to the witch, Molly was often in the company of Benning Wentworth, yet some instinct caused her to turn aside the governor's entreaties for an early marriage. However, time was on his side. The girl was indebted to him for many gifts and favors. Her beloved Richard had been gone for more than a year. One evening, she told her father that she would marry the lonely old governor. Benning was in Boston. When he returned they would make the announcement.

That same evening a horseman riding north on the Post Road was forced to dismount from his jaded beast. He had driven the horse hard. Now she was exhausted. The man removed his saddle and led the tired animal toward Portsmouth. It was late when he reached Sagamore Road. Arriving at the Pittman farm, he let the horse loose in a grazing field and walked toward the dark and silent farmhouse. He knocked at the door and waited. Several minutes later, Hosea Pittman opened the door, his musket cocked and ready in his hands.

"Put down your gun Mr. Pittman," the stranger said. "It's me—Richard Shortridge.

There was no more sleep that night in the Pittman home. Rosy-cheeked Molly and her father listened to the adventures which had befallen Richard. He told of being waylaid on Sagamore Road by a navy press gang, of his trials as a sailor in the King's Navy. He talked of his escape from New Providence, and the warmhearted generosity of Captain Polk of the brig *Boston Hope*.

The following day Richard Shortridge and Molly Pittman posted banns of marriage in Portsmouth. Molly collected her gifts and sent them back to Governor Wentworth without explanation. Although Richard was certain that Wentworth had been instrumental in his capture by the press gang, he decided to say nothing about it to his friends.

The couple were married but stayed in Portsmouth only until Richard completed his term as an apprentice. Then they moved to Salem where their descendants live to this day.

A sequel to this tale took place but a few months later. In Governor Benning Wentworth's household at Little Harbor lived a young Irish servant by the name of Martha Hilton. She was eighteen, pert and pretty with milk-white skin, black hair and flashing dark eyes. She was a happy, carefree girl who mayhap was a bit careless in her dress, wanting in modesty, and who left much to be desired as a domestic; nevertheless, everyone loved her charming, elving spirit.

In Longfellow's "Tales of a Wayside Inn," an innkeeper's wife upbraided the girl for her careless bearing in this manner: "Martha Hilton! How dare you go about town half-dressed like an immodest gypsy."

The girl replied: "No matter how I look now, someday I shall ride my own carriage dressed as a lady."

One evening in March, Governor Wentworth gave a birthday party at the great house. It was to celebrate his sixtieth birthday. All of the socially prominent people of the colony attended. There were the Pepperells, the Langdons, the Sparhawks and the Lears as well as many lesser socialites.

After many expressions of felicitations to their host, the party entered the beautiful stateroom. There a table glistening with glass and silver and laden with a rich variety of foods was ready for the banquet. When the party was seated, the Reverend Arthur Browne, rector of the Queen's Chapel of Portsmouth, was at the right hand of the royal governor.

After the dinner had been served and consumed, after toasts had been drunk to the King, the host whispered to a servant who nodded and left the room. In a moment he returned, followed by Martha Hilton. The girl, a blush on her cheeks and a roguish smile in her Irish eyes, stood demurely behind the governor's chair. Benning Wentworth arose from his chair and his guests watched expectantly.

"On this happy occasion, I have an announcement to make. Today, on my sixtieth birthday, I am about to be wed." He reached out and took Martha's hand. "My friends, I want you to meet the future Lady Wentworth."

The socially minded guests stared in surprise and some embarrassment at the servant girl, still wearing the clothes of a domestic, standing beside the old governor.

Wentworth turned to the guest on his right. "Reverend Mr. Browne, will you please marry us."

The stunned clergyman stammered and choked. The governor's temper boiled over.

"Yes, damn it! Marry us at once."

Thus, with the cream of New Hampshire society looking on, Martha Hilton, servant girl, became the Lady Wentworth, wife of Royal Governor Benning Wentworth.

The Duel

One evening in the spring of 1760, in a large tavern near the outskirts of Montreal, a group of officers of the famous Black Watch were making merry. Why not! Had they not defeated Montcalm's Army of Quebec and then overwhelmed another powerful French and Canadian army at Three Rivers. Now a great country was in their grasp. They were victors, and to the victors belong the spoils.

The atmosphere in the tavern was congenial. Wine, cider and rum were available for a modest penny. Moreover, three plump young geese were turning on spits before the great fireplace, sending a delectable aroma throughout the room. Drippings from the cooking fowl fell on the hot coals, flaring up in shreds of flame, sending flashes of light across the dimly lit room, reflecting on the burnished surfaces of pewter and brass utensils and casting grotesque shadows over the faces of the convivial patrons.

The tavern door opened and a tall, slim man dressed in faded buckskins entered and stood for a moment leaning on a long rifle as he glanced over the company. When he sighted the tartan and bonnets of the officers of the Black Watch, a smile creased his tanned face. Quickly, walking with effortless strides, he made his way across the room and presented himself before them. After bowing courteously, he spoke.

"I believe that you gentlemen are members of the Forty-second Regiment. I am Thomas Maverick of Boston, a captain of Provincial Rangers. Your colonel, Mr. Campbell, suggested for my entertainment that I join you."

The officers of the Scottish regiment, with smiling faces, arose, shook hands with the stranger and welcomed him heartily to their circle. Their was one exception. A beefy, red-faced major ignored his hand.

"A Yankee!" he exclaimed. His tone was an insult.

His fellow officers, embarrassed and ill-at-ease, did a creditable job in covering the major's breach of good manners and hospitality. However, his presence and evident disapproval of the Yankee captain created an air of tension. The easy camaraderie of the other officers with the Bostonian was tempered by the knowledge that Major James Sutherland was a dangerous and unpredictable man. He was a sadistic killer who successfully legalized his murders by prating of his honor and making use of the duel to accomplish his evil designs. Deadly with sword and pistol, he had killed several opponents since his arrival in Canada with his regiment. Invariably he had provoked the quarrels, stirring the anger of his victims with a caustic tongue until forced to challenge him to a duel. Three of his opponents had been New Englanders. On the so-called field of honor he killed them, coldly, without mercy. The junior officers of the army hated, feared and despised him.

As the evening wore on, the major drank steadily, refusing to enter into conversation with their guest. However, the New Englander, friendly and apparently at ease, swapped stories of wars and campaigns with his hosts.

"I was commander of a company in front of Ticonderoga when General Abercromby tried to capture the place," he told them. "The French defenses were strong and cunningly hidden. They cut us to pieces with a cross fire of grapeshot from well-concealed cannon until we were forced to retreat."

Major Sutherland broke in, his voice poisonous with malice. "I presume you were leading a company of rascally Yankees. 'Tis little wonder that General Abercromby was defeated. Yankee cowardice won that battle for the French."

"You, sir, are a damn liar," Maverick said quietly.

The group of officers stared in consternation as the major, with a grim smile, stood and leaned toward the Bostonian, his knuckles pressed on the table. "Sir! I demand redress. My word and honor have been impugned. Are you man enough to meet me on the field of honor. Perhaps I should first ask if a Yankee understands the meaning of honor."

White with fury, Captain Maverick leaped to his feet. "I'll meet you, any time or place, with one proviso—that we meet alone, without seconds."

Instantly the major protested. "Nay, man, that is against all dueling rules. It's highly irregular."

"Are you afraid?" asked the Yankee with a sneer.

This time it was Sutherland who showed his anger. "Damn you! I will meet you tomorrow morning at six o'clock in the field behind Nogent's blacksmith shop."

Captain Maverick nodded. "I'll be there."

"If you run as fast as most Yankees," the major snapped, "I fear you will be far away by tomorrow morning." Bowing with exaggerated courtliness, he left the room.

After he had gone, the officers of the Black Watch urged their guest to ignore the challenge. "It will not be a fair fight," they told him. "The major is without a peer in swordplay or targets."

The Bostonian thanked them for their concern. "Do not worry, gentlemen. I have no intention of laying down my life for a few foolish words. I have a plan which might well discomfit and teach the major a needed lesson. If you gentlemen will go to the field early and conceal yourselves in the blacksmith shop where you can observe the duel without being seen, I will endeavor to show you an unusual trial of honor."

Early the following morning, the officers of the Black Watch entered the blacksmith shop and congregated near an open loft door which overlooked the field.

Shortly before six o'clock Captain Maverick strolled onto the field, still dressed in buckskins. Under his arm was his rifle. Leaning thoughtfully on it, he surveyed the deserted streets.

Punctually at six o'clock, Major James Sutherland appeared, armed with his sword and carrying a brace of dueling pistols in a case. As he approached, the Yankee lifted his rifle and aimed it at the Scotchman.

"Stop where you are," he commanded, "or I will blow your brains out."

"Why you damnable villain. What is the meaning of this?" asked the startled major.

Maverick motioned with the gun barrel. "Lay your sword and pistols on the ground. Lively now!"

The choleric Sutherland obeyed, all the while cursing the Bostonian.

"You are a knave, without the honor of a worm. You have proved yourself a coward—a Yankee coward."

"You prate about honor and courage," Captain Maverick sneered. "Here, my brave fellow. Take my rifle."

With a quick heave, he tossed his weapon to the major. Sutherland, a look of savage exultation on his face, lifted the gun, pointing it at Maverick. For several moments he stood with the gun aimed at the Bostonian, while he jeered at the captain.

"You are a fool. You should have shot me when you had the opportunity. Now I shall blow your head off."

"Blow away and be damned," Maverick retorted contemptuously. "You are naught but a sneaking murderer."

In an excess of passion, Major Sutherland aimed at the Yankee and pulled the trigger. Nothing happened. Frantically he pulled back the hammer and tried again but the gun refused to fire.

From the door of the blacksmith shop came angry calls. "For shame! For shame! Dare you shoot at an unarmed man. Where is your honor."

The major turned and stared in amazement and shame at his fellow officers standing in the doorway of the smithy.

"You have proved yourself to be a man without honor," Captain Maverick told him.

Dropping the rifle, Major Sutherland ran, ran as if pursued by the fiend.

The following day he sold his commission and left the army.

The battle that Maverick referred to, which led to a sharp exchange and the challenge of a duel with Major Sutherland, was fought for the possession of Fort Ticonderoga in 1758. It ended in one of the worst defeats suffered by the British Army in America.

General Abercromby with fifteen thousand men assailed the fortifications of Ticonderoga for four hours. The fort was defended by an inferior force of French and Canadian soldiers under the command of General Montcalm. The French, well entrenched, cut down the advancing Redcoats and Provincial regiments until they were forced to retreat, leaving behind two thousand brave men who died on the blood-soaked field.

Stonewall Silas Clapp

The frailties of the human race are many. Some men are addicted to strong drink, gambling, the pursuit of money or fame. Some strive to become artists or writers. But Silas Clapp the Younger, of Warwick, Rhode Island, possessed a stranger obsession. He had an overruling passion for building stone walls.

Sometime around the year 1802 the widow of Silas Clapp the Elder, who owned considerable land in Rhode Island, deeded a tract of land in Cowesett to her nephew, Silas Clapp, who was designated "the Younger." It was to be a wedding present. It appeared that the young man wished to marry and settle down.

Silas the Younger must have been an energetic and ambitious man, for he began at once to build a large twelve-room house on his lot.

Some Yankees of that day began their married life with a small house and built additions to it as their families increased. Silas evidently figured on having a large family and built for the future. He spent every farthing he owned and was stone-broke when the house was finally finished.

Then came the turning point of his life. He contracted to build a stone wall for his neighbor, Thomas Greene. Field stones were plentiful and he built a magnificent wall, strong and straight, the stones cunningly laid in such a manner that each added strength to the completed structure. High praise from Mr. Greene, Mr. Waterman and other neighbors infused a glow of honest pride in the breast of Silas.

With the money obtained by these labors, Silas went looking for a wife. In the village of Wickford he met a vivacious young lady whose twinkling eyes, shapely ankles and other feminine attributes sparked a glow of love in his manly heart. Opposites attract. Silas the Younger was a silent, staid, sober young man, while Rhoda Andrews of Wickford was a talkative, fun-loving, happy-hearted girl. Silas wooed, won and married her. They started their married life in his newly built house.

To obtain the means of supporting his household, Silas began to build stone walls. He neglected his farm to build them. In a short time he acquired local fame as the best stone wall builder in Rhode Island. Although he worked long hours, his labors scarcely kept food in the larder. But he was content. He had discovered a mission in life—to clear rocks and boulders from acres of potentially rich farmland and fence them in geometric patterns with sturdy stone walls. Money was not everything in life.

This viewpoint was not shared by his wife. A gossip by nature, Rhoda found the loneliness and daily toil on the Clapp farm almost unbearable.

Time passed, and the large family Silas had hoped to produce did not materialize. The empty rooms in the Clapp house remained unoccupied. The couple saw their neighbors' families grow yearly with wondrous regularity while they remained childless.

After they had been married for a few years, Rhoda urged Silas to turn their large house into a tavern. They lived only a short distance from the turnpike. Every day, stagecoaches traveled to and fro between New London, Connecticut, and Providence. The small tavern in Crompton had few accommodations, while they had many fine rooms. She pointed out to him that they might reap rich financial rewards for such a venture. Secretly she thought of it as a means of combatting loneliness. She envisioned the bustle and excitement of stagecoaches arriving and departing, of men and women travelers dressed in the latest fashions, of the opportunity to meet and speak with someone other than her monosyllabic spouse.

Her dreams shattered on the rocklike stubbornness of Silas the Younger. He would never allow his home to become an inn where his role of master could be challenged by the whims of strangers. "No, by Godfrey!"

So the adamant Silas continued to build stone walls, gleaning field stones from unworked acres, heaving them into his two-wheeled cart and transporting them to the wall sites. At home he seldom spoke. Rhoda, seeking the companionship of conversation, would talk to him for hours, asking him questions, trying vainly to arouse him to speech. He ignored the poor woman, ate his supper, sat down to thumb through his Bible. Later, after carrying in the firewood for the next day, he would retire. Rhoda once likened him to the big stupid horse that dragged his two-wheeled cart.

This way of life became more than Rhoda could bear. One day she packed her belongings and left the Clapp house. In the village of Crompton she secured a job in the local tavern which catered to a number of farmers, woodsmen and millworkers.

When Silas arrived home that evening, he fed his horse, searched the house for Rhoda, cooked his own supper, carried in the wood and read his Bible as usual. After four weeks of bachelorhood, and possibly prodded by unwashed dishes and dirty clothes, he decided to pursue his wife. Driving to Crompton in his cart, he dismounted, walked into the tavern and confronted her.

"You are my wife. No more nonsense. Pack your things. You're coming home with me," he told her in probably the longest speech he had uttered in years.

Unfortunately for him Mrs. Clapp was unwilling to obey his command. When he grasped her arm and pulled to emphasize his determination, Rhoda appealed to her employer for protection. The tavernkeeper tried to push Silas out of the door. Silas refused to be pushed. In fact, he refused so strenuously that the proprietor was tossed through his own tavern door, to land ignominiously in the horse droppings beneath the hitching rack. It took a constable, a deputy sheriff and two husky citizens to subdue the stone wall builder and contain him in the local jail. The next day an unsympathetic judge fined him ten dollars. Sadly Silas Clapp returned home—alone.

For the next three years Silas lived alone in the big house, concentrating his energy on his mission, building stone walls in Rhode Island and Connecticut. It was a matter of pride with him that the Fence Viewers, appointed by the several towns where he erected walls, had never criticized his workmanship.

His mission ended abruptly one morning while he was loading stones in his cart. A worn strap on the traces broke and the cart tipped. Silas was found with the tailgate of the cart resting on his chest, his head hidden from sight beneath a load of field stones. He was dead.

He was buried on the brow of a slope overlooking the bustling New London turnpike. His neighbors appropriately built a cairn of field stones to mark his grave. For years the cairn was a landmark for travelers on the highway.

In the 1940s the state of Rhode Island widened and straightened the old turnpike. A retaining wall was needed at the base of a steep slope. So the stones of the cairn on the unmarked grave of the stone wall builder were used to build a wall. It is a sturdy, well-built wall, a fitting monument for Silas Clapp the Younger.

This story comes from family tradition. Unfortunately there is no information of what became of Mrs. Silas Clapp after the demise of her estimable spouse.

Giant of the Green Mountains

There was a crowd in the taproom of the Catamount Tavern that warm May night in 1775. There were trappers from the mountains who had sold their fur pelts for hard cash and were now spending it for rum. There were woodsmen who had spent a winter clearing land, burning trees and leaching wood ashes for potash, a readily salable product on the frontier. There were impoverished homesteaders, most of them a shiftless lot, who had lived through the long winter cooped up in their isolated cabins and were now in town to barter their few pitiful possessions for rum. And leaning against the bar which occupied half the length of the room were two bounty hunters in stained, dirty buckskins, wilder looking than the painted Indians of the Northwest and smelling worse than any ignorant savage.

Tavernkeeper Stephen Fay smiled as he surveyed the scene. Rum and hard cider were flowing as the convivial frontiersmen attempted to wash away the memories of hardships, of loneliness and dull monotony which had been their lot during the drear winter. Hard cash was accumulating in the till, and bartered products were piling up in the storerooms. Fay had reason to be happy.

Suddenly a loud voice thundered above the din, a sonorous

voice that easily carried to every corner of the room. All eyes turned toward the bar where a giant of a man, hands on his hips, was bitterly cursing the two bounty hunters.

"Damn your stinking, sniveling, worthless hides," he roared. "So you spent the winter in the Onion River country. My friend Elijah Doty tells me that you are Yorkers and you have hired out as guides to a rotten, bug-crawling, white-livered York surveyor."

The big man dramatically spread his arms as he turned to search the faces of the other patrons in the room. There were many tall men in the taproom that night, but this giant towered over them by a head. He was dressed like a frontier dandy in beautifully tanned doeskin trousers and shirt, brightly decorated with quill and bead work. Encircling his waist was a Mohawk belt and pouch. A luxuriant shock of curly brown hair cascaded from beneath a small, round fur cap, ornamented by a single bright red eagle feather.

"Did you hear what these 'rattlesnakes' expect to do?" he asked the spectators. "They intend to guide a York surveyor into the Grants. They don't know how we treat sneaks and land-grabbers around here."

His words provoked jeers and laughter. "Hang the buggers," a homesteader shouted.

Again the giant faced the bounty hunters, leaning toward them threateningly, his doubled-up fists half-raised, his jutting chin close to the faces of the would-be guides.

"I'm telling you," he said, his voice rough with passion, "that if I ever catch you helping a surveyor to steal our lands, if you ever take a penny from one of Governor Tryon's foul hell-hounds for services rendered, I, Ethan Allen, will take up the jawbone of an ass and smite the putrid scum that you use for brains from your stupid heads."

A deep silence settled over the room as the spectators watched avidly, expecting a brawl, for the bounty hunters were known as mean and truculent men even when sober. Now, with half a dozen drinks of rum under their belt, they were not likely to count consequences. One of them leaped back from Allen and pulled a long skinning knife from his belt, his eyes glowing with hate. The other reached for a wooden bucket full of sawdust which was on the floor by his feet. With bewildering speed the giant Allen leaped into action. One hand yanked the bucket of sawdust from the nearest hunter. Raising it in one motion, he hurled the pail and contents into the face of the knife wielder, knocking him to the floor. Then using fists and feet with deadly efficiency, Ethan battered his opponents into insensibility.

Fay motioned to two of his servants. Quickly they dragged the vanquished hunters from the room. There would be other fights before the evening was over, for most of his patrons were a lawless breed, unaccustomed to obeying any laws but those of their own choosing. He only hoped that there would be no killings.

A mug of rum laced with hard cider was thrust into Ethan's hand by a grinning young man in buckskins.

"By all that's holy!" Allen exclaimed. "If it isn't Remember Baker. I thought you were in the Winooski country. What the devil are you doing here?"

Remember moved closer to Ethan, suppressing excitement. "I didn't go north after our meeting at your brother Heman's house," he said softly. "I traveled to Hartford with Heman. We heard about the bloodletting at Concord and Lexington. The Committee was excited. They've begun to raise an army."

An eager light glowed in Ethan's eyes as he searched his cousin's face. "What did they say?" he asked. "Where is Heman?"

"Heman is down the road a spell. He will be here soon."

"Good! If my brother is coming to Bennington, he must have succeeded in getting that bunch of backside sitters on the

Hartford Committee to agree on my plan. Maybe now that blood has been shed, we shall have some action in this neck of the woods."

Remember nodded, a grin wrinkling his face. "Maybe we will," he agreed.

The door of the tavern swung open and a rugged, bearded man stood in the doorway, a smile of triumph on his leathery face. He wore a long green coat and a green cocked hat adorned with a large red, white and blue rosette. A pair of soiled brown trousers and stained white stockings showed the effects of hard traveling on muddy trails.

"Gentlemen! Gentlemen!" he shouted, waving his arms for attention. Slowly the din in the taproom quieted.

"Heman, you old bugger!" Ethan bawled.

The man in the doorway waved at him, then focused his attention on his audience.

"Gentlemen, I have just arrived from Hartford," he announced. I have a letter from the Connecticut Committee of Correspondence requesting Colonel Ethan Allen of the Grants to raise a force of Green Mountain Boys and capture the King's forts at Ticonderoga and Crown Point."

Silence enveloped the tavern as the patrons digested this astonishing news. Many of them had come from Massachusetts, but they had lived for many years on the frontier, almost untouched by the King's laws. The reasons for all the political turmoil that had finally broken out into active rebellion in the coastal towns and cities were only vaguely understood by them. They had a healthy respect for the well-trained soldiers of the King's Army and could not yet believe that a mob of farmers had been able to defeat them. Furthermore, they had been taught from infancy that anyone who damaged the King's properties would be punished severely.

Ethan Allen noticed the thoughtful mien of the men in the tavern. Leaping onto a table, he emitted a bloodcurdling scream. "We're going on a wolf hunt," he roared. "Anyone who is ten feet tall and able to shoot the whiskers off of the Devil is welcome to go. Tomorrow we will begin to assemble an army of heroes. Then we're going to cross the lake and chase every red-livered bugger in Ticonderoga all the way to Canada. Whee!"

The mercurial frontiersmen forgot their doubts and roared approval. Ethan Allen had a way with him.

Ethan Allen, controversial and legendary figure of old New England, was born in Litchfield, Connecticut, on the tenth day of January in 1737, the first son of Joe and Mary Baker Allen. In subsequent years the Allens had seven more children. All but Ethan were born in Cornwall, Connecticut.

Like all children born on the frontier, Ethan had to work from the day he could walk, yet he still found time to hunt and fish—and read. He read every book he could lay his hands on. His thirst for knowledge impressed his father, who sent him to the Reverend Johnathan Lee for schooling. However, his father died before he could complete his studies, and he returned home.

At the age of nineteen Ethan turned over management of the Allen farm to his younger brothers and enlisted in a company that was being organized to fight the French and their Indian allies. With his comrades he marched to Lake George, arriving too late to aid in the defense of Fort William Henry. In a short time he was back on the farm. But now he was restless. He dabbled in real estate and tried his hand at running an iron furnace. He was reaching manhood now—a tall, handsome youth who loved socials and an occasional bundling party. Records show that he was quarrelsome and profane. He landed in court on several occasions. About this time he began to dream of owning large tracts of land in the Hampshire Grants.

The Hampshire Grants was a huge area of disputed land

Viking ships head for the unknown perils of a new world.

Leif Ericson and his Norsemen land on the New England Coast.

The Old Colony Historical Society, Taunton, Mass.

Dighton Rock with its mysterious inscription

Robert E. Stone

A mysterious stone slab with deep-cut drainage grooves, believed to have been used for human sacrifices, found in North Salem, New Hampshire

Thomas Dustin of Haverhill, Massachusetts, rescues seven of his children from attacking Indians.

Colonel Ethan Allen and his Green Mountain Boys capture Fort Ticonderoga "in the name of the Great Jehovah and the Continental Congress." Engraving after a painting by Alonzo Chappel.

Major Robert Rogers who aroused the Curse of the Abenaki

Drawing by Howard Pyle illustrates a pirate, like Black Sam
Bellamy, forcing a prisoner to walk the plank.

The daily pursuits of the Indians, such as this hunt painted in *The Moose Chase* by George de Forest Brush, formed the basis of many an early New England legend.

lying between Lake George, Lake Champlain and the Connecticut River. Old Benning Wentworth, governor of New Hampshire, had been for years selling choice sections of this land to land companies despite the fact that New York and Massachusetts also claimed the area. A few settlements had been built on the disputed land along the Connecticut River. The only town west of the Connecticut Valley was a small town called Bennington. The rest of the country was a wilderness, most of it unmapped. Into this wilderness Ethan Allen went. He spent a winter on snowshoes, ranging over the Green Mountains and the Champlain Valley. He was in love with the country by the time he returned home.

However, clouds of strife were gathering over the disputed territory. The colony of New York protested to the King over Governor Wentworth's land sales and set forth their own claims to the land. In 1764 the King acknowledged New York's claim. At once Governor Colden of that colony sent surveyors into the disputed land and began to make grants to his friends, grants of land which were already occupied by frontiersmen who had bought their land in good faith from Governor Wentworth's land promoters. The law was on the side of the New York grantees. The occupants of the land resisted. They threatened and assaulted the New York surveyors and even their sheriffs. Into this strife came Ethan Allen and took command of the Wentworth grantees who called themselves the Green Mountain Boys. Their headquarters was the Catamount Tavern in Bennington.

Tryon, who succeeded Colden as governor of New York, intensified pressure on the settlers. After several small riots in which York sympathizers were whipped and forced to leave the Grants, Governor Tryon outlawed Ethan Allen and five of his Boys, offering a reward of twenty pounds for their arrest.

Meanwhile, Ethan Allen and his brothers bought a large

tract in the Winooski Valley. They formed a company and began to sell land. Then they began to worry over the proximity of Fort Ticonderoga.

Fort Ticonderoga, that great stone bastion which effectively guarded the narrows of Lake Champlain, had had a long and bloody history. It was built by the French in 1755 and named Fort Carillon. Within easy access to the Hudson Valley it at once posed a threat to the English colonies. The English in 1758 tried to take the fort and were soundly defeated. After the Peace of Paris it fell into the hands of the British and was renamed Ticonderoga. Since that time it had been allowed to fall into disrepair. A small garrison occupied the fort in 1775 under the command of Captain Delaplace. The present garrison posed no threat to the Allen land company, but if the fort was reinforced by New Yorkers the company would be placed in a dangerous situation. Governor Tryon would like nothing better than an opportunity to strike back at the Allens.

Ticonderoga and its threat to his land company must have come often to Ethan's mind. At a directors' meeting of the company in Sheffield it was openly discussed. The directors decided to send Heman to Hartford to confer with the Committee of Correspondence and to sound them out about a possible attack on the fort by the Green Mountain Boys in the event that hostilities took place anywhere in the colonies.

The bloody events at Lexington and Concord made his mission unnecessary. As he was about to return home, Heman was approached by members of the Committee and asked to convey a letter to his brother Ethan, asking him to lead an attack on Fort Ticonderoga and promising to send money for supplies. Heman wasted no time. Changing horses frequently, he headed for Bennington and the Catamount Tavern.

With his usual energy Ethan Allen began to round up his Boys. Messengers rode away in all directions from Bennington. Guards were placed on the roads leading to Fort Edwards,

Lake George, Skenesboro, Ticonderoga and Crown Point to intercept any Royalists who might try to warn the British of the impending attack. Three days after Heman's arrival, Noah Phelps, Bernard Romans and Edward Mott rode into Bennington, bringing with them the money promised for supplies.

On the morning of May 8 a council of war was held at Castleton. Edward Mott of Connecticut was elected chairman. It was agreed that the expedition against Ticonderoga should be under the command of Ethan Allen. Samuel Herrick with thirty men was sent to Skenesboro to take into custody Colonel Skene's family and servants. The colonel was a retired officer of the British Army and was not to be trusted. Skene's boats were to be sent down the lake under cover of darkness to meet Ethan Allen and his Boys at Hand's Cove and transport them across the lake.

It was a wild-looking company of frontiersmen who assembled at Hand's Cove. There were men from Massachusetts and Connecticut as well as the Green Mountain Boys. With little attempt at secrecy, they lit campfires and cooked their meals. They wrestled and sang without restraint. All night the late-comers came walking into camp. Toward morning an officer, wearing the scarlet coat of a Connecticut Guard Regiment and accompanied by a servant, rode into camp.

He was a handsome, proud-looking man. With insolent pomp he introduced himself to the officers as Captain Benedict Arnold and requested Colonel Ethan Allen to turn over the command of the expedition to him.

Can you not picture the scene? The elegant, aristocratic gamecock, Benedict Arnold, facing the Green Mountain Giant, Ethan Allen, a man quick to anger, ready to fight and filled with an egotistical belief in his own destiny. Probably Ethan, with his mastery of a salty and profane vocabulary, told the captain no, using several sentences to emphasize his answer. I picture the brave and passionate Arnold whipping out his sword and demanding satisfaction, his face white and twisted with wrath. Alas, no historian was present to record the scene. The Green Mountain Boys would restrain the angry captain who wished to commit suicide by tangling with their leader. Benedict Arnold was forced to swallow his wrath. Perhaps Ethan Allen, generous in his strength, offered the captain a subordinate command. Whatever happened, Benedict Arnold was one of the Colonials who dared the King's wrath by assaulting one of his strongholds.

Dawn was approaching when an old scow and a large whaleboat finally arrived at Hand's Cove. There were about two hundred men waiting on the shore. Eighty-five men crowded into the two vesesls, dangerously overloading them. The moon had set and squalls were blowing up over the lake. Seth Warner was left in command of the rear guard, and the two boats shoved off from shore. With amazing luck they made the opposite shore with nothing more than wet feet. There was not enough time for the boats to return to Hand's Cove for reinforcements. The officers gave low-voiced orders, and the men began to march toward Fort Ticonderoga. Ethan and Benedict Arnold led the column, both dressed in uniform. The rest of the men marched in their working clothes.

It was still dark when the assailants reached the outer defenses of the fort. A guard saw them as they rushed forward in wild disorder. He cocked his musket and pulled the trigger but the gun misfired. Taking to his heels, he ran toward the barracks shouting wildly to awaken the garrison. Ethan rushed after him, and his men, with Indian war whoops, followed. Like wolves they dashed into the barracks and captured the stunned and sleepy soldiers of the garrison. One of the prisoners led Ethan to a stairway leading to the commandant's room. A lieutenant appeared at the head of the stairs, holding his breeches in his hands. Ethan with Arnold by his side started up the stairs. The lieutenant motioned for them to halt, asking by what authority they entered His Majesty's fort. Ethan, his voice hoarse with excitement, shouted, "In the name of the Great Jehovah and the Continental Congress." Another door on the upper floor opened and the commandant, Captain Delaplace stepped out. Without resistance he handed his sword to Ethan and ordered his men to be paraded without arms.

In this manner Colonel Ethan Allen and his Green Mountain Boys captured Fort Ticonderoga. A great episode in American history had been accomplished. And out of the obscurity of a wilderness into the limelight of history stepped a Green Mountain Giant, Ethan Allen. In later years, under his guidance, there emerged from the disputed lands the Green Mountain State—Vermont. With Fort Ticonderoga were captured fourteen mortars, two howitzers, forty-three cannon, two tons of cannon and musket balls and an unrecorded amount of powder. These military supplies were transported to Boston, where they were instrumental in forcing the British to evacuate that city.

LEGENDS

OF DEVILISH DOINGS,

OF WITCHES,

HAUNTED HOUSES AND

OTHER SUPERNATURAL THINGS.

Lady Eaton's Curse

This tale is made of many ingredients, of stern religious bigotry, of hardships suffered in an inhospitable wilderness, of envy and hate and a madness induced by cruel ostracism.

It began in England when the Reverend John Davenport, an intolerant and irascible Puritan preacher, was forced to leave his native land because of his outspoken criticism of church and state. Several of his parishioners decided to follow him into exile. They chartered a ship and, with their families, servants and a few precious possessions, sailed for the wilderness of New England. In 1638 they founded a colony which they named New Haven, buying the land from local Indian sachems.

In the eyes of the jealous Pilgrims at Plymouth and the ambitious Dutch at New Amsterdam, they were interlopers. However, they were not interested in the opinions of their neighbors. Without charter or permission from the New England Council, they built their homes, their meetinghouse, their fort, and ruled their settlement solely by the laws given in the Scriptures.

One of these adventurous colonists was Thiophilus Eaton, a wealthy, distinguished and well-educated gentleman, a close friend and disciple of Davenport's.

Eaton's life had been a succession of brilliant attainments. In his youth, an influential nobleman, impressed by his eager intelligence, sent him to a famous university where he acquired an excellent education. After his graduation he secured a job as clerk in a large mercantile house. Within a short time he became an agent for the firm, traveling extensively in France and Holland. Later he became an agent for the King of England to the King of Denmark. He married a lady of high degree and took her with him to Copenhagen, where they lived for many years in the luxurious surroundings of the Danish court. Two children were born to them, first a son, and several years later a daughter. Their idyllic life in the gay capital of Copenhagen ended abruptly. Lady Eaton was stricken with brain fever and died. Soon after, Thiophilus and his two children returned to England and settled in London, where he founded a mercantile company. His mother came to live with him, taking over the management of his house and family.

He was forty-one years old when he met Anne, the beautiful and talented daughter of the Bishop of Chester. She was seventeen, only two years older than his son. Her fresh, youthful charm captivated him. He was wealthy, courtly and still a very handsome man. The romantic young girl, yielding to his entreaties, became the second Lady Eaton.

Like all brides, she dreamed of a happy, useful future as wife and partner, sharing her husband's life, mothering his children and supervising his household. This was not to be. As the second wife of Thiophilus Eaton, fate had placed her in an intolerable position. She had scarcely become acquainted with her new home before the Puritan pastor, John Davenport, began to call daily, pressing her to renounce Episcopalianism and accept the stern tenets of Puritanism. He was blunt of speech and cruelly critical of her father, the Bishop, and all that he stood for. When she remonstrated to her husband, he coldly informed her that she must accept the Puritan precepts. Sadly but obediently she assented to the spiritual guidance of the Reverend Mr. Davenport.

When the young bride tried to supervise the servants and manage the household, she met with opposition and resentment. Instigated by her stepchildren, the servants were insolent and surly. Furthermore, Thiophilus's mother, the elder Mrs. Eaton, resented and hated the girl, doing everything possible to undermine her wifely authority. When in the course of time Anne gave birth to two children, a boy and a girl, the elder Mrs. Eaton persuaded her son to place them in her care. Anne realized that her mother-in-law was attempting to steal the love of her children and appealed to her husband, only to have him treat her as a jealous child. Only then did she understand that the difference in their ages was a barrier to understanding.

When the decree of banishment was received by Pastor John Davenport, he hastened to secure passage in a ship bound for Boston in the New World. Eaton and several other influential members of his congregation promised to follow him. They spent several months disposing of their properties in England. Early in 1638 they chartered a ship and sailed toward New England where they could worship according to the dictates of their hearts.

The trip across the broad Atlantic was a succession of wild storms, sudden alarms and constant prayer. Stagnant water, stale bread, the odor of unwashed bodies and the cramped quarters in one small cabin seared the soul of young Mrs. Eaton. They paused briefly in Boston where Davenport joined them. Several days later they landed on the wooded banks of the Quinnipiac River and began to build their settlement. Thiophilus Eaton was elected to be their first governor. Charles Greyson was appointed magistrate and Pastor Davenport became interpreter of the laws as well as ecclesiastical leader.

Work and prayer became the constant preoccupation of the

settlers. They fished, hunted and farmed the land for suste-nance, but few became adept at these pursuits. The future appeared bleak. In the first twelve months the settlement was distinguished by only a small wooden meetinghouse, two dwellings of some pretention, homes of the Davenports and Eatons, and a scattering of rude shelters which housed the other settlers. These were huddled on each side of a wide dirt road which ended on the shore where a stone landing had been built. However, hard toil began to transform the settlement, which was named New Haven, into a fairly comfortable and prosperous place. The leaders of the colony hoped that their small town might someday become a great seaport, perhaps the commercial center of the New World. They decided to pool their resources, build a large ship, fill it with furs, lumber and sassafras bark, and send it to England where the cargo could be exchanged for products needed in the colony. Plans for the ship were drawn, and the great undertaking was started on the shores of the Quinnipiac River.

Lady Anne Eaton lost her youth in the new land. She worked hard, asserted her authority as mistress of the house and punished her servants for the least infraction of her rules. With her mother-in-law and stepchildren she lived in an un-easy truce. Her only enjoyment was playing with her own children. Her relations with Thiophilus gradually deteriorated into a formal politeness. After their house was furnished, the governor slept on a cot in his study, leaving Anne alone in the bedroom. She avoided Davenport and Charles Greyson, who impressed her as the prince of hypocrites.

In the spring the Eatons entertained a visitor, Lady Moody, a woman of Salem who was traveling to New Amsterdam. Lady Anne became quite friendly with their guest. Mrs. Moody confided to Anne that she had been excommunicated from the Church of Salem for her opposition to child baptism. The two women talked long and earnestly about their religious beliefs. When Mrs. Moody left New Haven, she gave Lady Eaton several religious tracts which had been published by a secret group of freethinkers in the Massachusetts colony.

One Sunday afternoon Governor Eaton, as was his custom, assembled the members of his household and, with Lady Anne at his side, led them to the meetinghouse. In this combination town hall, courthouse and church the members were seated according to rank. In the first pew sat the governor and his lady, their children and the elder Mrs. Eaton. In the second pew sat the Greysons and their three children.

The Reverend John Davenport opened the meeting with a prayer, which was followed by a sermon by Mr. Hooke, a forceful speaker who years later became chaplain to Oliver Cromwell.

After the sermon the pastor announced that the rite of baptism would be administered to two children. Abruptly Lady Anne Eaton arose from her seat and, with head held high, passed down the aisle and out of the door. A murmur of surprise rippled through the congregation. Many eyes fastened on the governor, but Eaton, his face showing no emotion, sat through the service of baptism.

In such a tightly knit community it was inevitable that Lady Eaton's action would be discussed and jealous minds would speak out against her. Mrs. Greyson, who had long envied the beautiful Lady Anne, spoke critically of her un-Christian behavior. She urged her husband to seek out the reason for her Ladyship's boycott of the baptism service.

The following evening Magistrate Greyson called at the governor's house and accepted an invitation to remain for dinner. When the Eatons and their guest were seated at the table, the governor bowed his head and led the group in devotion. After a short prayer the family raised their bowed heads. Anne, seated beside her mother-in-law, murmured an "Amen."

"I rejoice daughter," said old Mrs. Eaton spitefully, "that

you have decided to receive God's Word with meekness." Lady Anne turned and, with no warning, struck the old woman twice in the face. Thiophilous, his features white with anger, seized his wife's hand and led her from the room.

Through the able efforts of Mrs. Greyson, the story of Lady Eaton's assault on her mother-in-law was soon known to everyone in the colony.

The following Sunday Anne Eaton did not attend worship services, and her husband offered no excuse for her absence. Rumors that Lady Eaton was an Anabaptist began to gain credence in New Haven, so Mr. Davenport, Mr. Hooke and Magistrate Greyson visited the governor's house to investigate. They found, on questioning the household, that Lady Anne had been abusing her servants, had shown disrespect to the words of Pastor Davenport, had struck the elder Mrs. Eaton and Mary Eaton and had committed several other misdemeanors, all showing an ungodly temper.

The sanctimonious Mr. Greyson urged her to repent before her sins were brought before the congregation for judgment.

"I deny," exclaimed Lady Eaton, "that you, Mr. Greyson, possess any right to concern yourself with my conscience, with my method of worshipping God or with the discipline in my home. This matter is between me and the congregation. It is not within the jurisdiction of a magistrate."

"It is the good of your soul, Mrs. Eaton, that I desire with all servants of Christ," answered Mr. Greyson.

Lady Eaton's beautiful eyes flashed. "It is not the good of my soul you desire, Mr. Greyson. I have oft noted your eyes wander toward me with a boldness and lust that are truly not seemly in a servant of the Lord."

Greyson's face flushed with anger. "So be it, my lady. The congregation shall decide your guilt."

It must have been an impressive scene, the primitive meetinghouse with its small, diamond-shaped window panes and the plain wooden benches filled with the citizens of the colony. Facing the congregation, behind a plain pine table, sat the Reverend John Davenport. He was a tall, gaunt man with deep-set eyes, a pallid skin and thin bloodless lips. His hose, waistcoat and knee breeches were a rusty black. Beside him sat the bulky, square-faced Mr. Hooke and a frail, white-haired cleric from Saybrook.

The long list of charges was read, and Lady Eaton stood up proudly, facing her husband, her children, her fellow colonists. A murmur was heard in the crowded room. The amber light of May draped Anne Eaton like a benediction. Her brilliant eyes shone with an inner light; her fingertips rested lightly on a string of white beads which emphasized the perfect column of her neck. Her cap of rich lace and a velvet dress with a wide lace collar set off the strange beauty of her features. She began to talk, to tell of her happy youth in England, of her father, the Bishop, of her sisters and their love for one another.

"Daughter," Pastor Davenport said sternly, "these are empty words."

The congregation, which had been touched with pity by her beauty and youth, quickly suppressed such sinful feelings. One after another, under the penetrating eyes of the pastor, they voted to censure and excommunicate the governor's wife. Then, in the darkening room, John Davenport pronounced the sentence which expelled her from the congregation and from any gathering of God's enlightened children.

From that day on, the Lady Anne was treated worse than a leper. The women of the town who had once greeted her with smiles and friendly words now passed her by with averted faces. The men ignored her when they came to the governor's house on business. Like a lonely wraith, the lovely woman moved about her home or took long walks through the fields.

One evening she arrived home from one of these rambles and found Mr. Greyson in conference with her husband.

"I trust, Mrs. Eaton," he said when she entered the room, "that after this long time, you have forgotten your anger toward me. What I did was for conscience sake. I would like your kind thoughts. Soon I will leave these shores to face the perils of the sea in the ship that is now abuilding."

"Forget the anger I bear you? Nay! How can it abate when every day my children, my family, my husband and my friends look upon me as an outcast. Mr. Greyson, you have made me an unloved and despised woman." She laughed wildly. "Should I give you peace on your coming voyage? No! But I will put you in God's keeping. May He give you in some small measure the despair that I feel each hour. May you be cast down in body and soul for your wicked deeds perpetrated in the name of conscience." She gave him a fierce glance of scorn and left the room.

The following winter was very severe. The harbor was frozen. When the great ship built by the colonists of New Haven was ready to sail, a channel had to be cut through the ice to the sea. Seventy souls embarked for the trip to England. Among them was Mrs. Goodyear, Captain Turner, Mr. Lamberton, master of the ship, and Mr. Greyson. When all was ready, the people knelt on the ice, and the Reverend John Davenport prayed for a safe and prosperous voyage. Then, amid tears and shouted salutations, the great ship sailed into the wintry Atlantic.

Nine or ten weeks was the average time for a passage to England in those early days. Time went by and nothing was heard of the ship. Anxiety and fear for the safety of the vessel were prevalent in New Haven when spring arrived and no news had been received of its arrival in England. Two more months went by, and hope turned to despair.

The governor's lady continued her restless walks, but now her path often took her to the shores of the harbor where she spent hours staring out toward the horizon. One day she was accosted by Mrs. Greyson.

"Why look you out to sea, Mistress," asked the magistrate's wife. "Are you gloating over my husband and the others whom you sent to death with your evil curse? Beware! One of these days the Devil will claim you."

One warm day in June a terrific thunderstorm flashed over New Haven, cooling the sultry air. A number of people were near the shore when a boy shouted shrilly.

"A ship! Here comes a brave ship."

Citizens stared in surprise and joy. Sailing before the wind with foam churning from her bow was Lamberton's ship. Signal guns were fired, and many people ceased their labors and ran to the beach. Among them was Governor Eaton.

Nearer and nearer sailed the ship. On the deck a man leaned over the rail and waved. People cried out in excitement. A hundred eyes were fastened on the incoming vessel. Suddenly, to their horror, the great mainmast swayed and fell in a welter of sails, ropes and spars. The top of the foremast broke, and the foresail, like a great curtain, fell over the bow. A cloud of smoke poured from the waist of the wrecked vessel. The amazed watchers saw the ship's stern rise slowly in the air and the craft plunge beneath the waves. The ship had sunk. Gentle waves rippled over the scene. Strangely no debris, no evidence of a wreck, was visible on the water. A phantom ship had entered the harbor and sank. A hundred colonists had witnessed the amazing event.

"It is God's way to show us what happened to our people," Pastor Davenport said.

The sky was the color of blood when the shaken crowd left the shore to return to their homes. On the main street another startling sight shook them. Their meetinghouse, hub of the settlement, was on fire and burning fiercely. Their was no hope of saving the structure. Shaken by the sight of the revealing mirage of their ship, and frightened by the loss of the meeting-house, the people hurried to their homes as if seeking safety behind friendly walls.

After a time a new and larger meetinghouse was built in New Haven. The elder Mrs. Eaton died. The harsh, Old Testament views of the administration were gradually replaced by tolerance and understanding. The Lady Anne resumed her rightful place in her home and community. The Reverend John Davenport with his family left New Haven and returned to Boston. When Thiophilus Eaton died, Lady Anne became the bulwark of the family. Under her guidance the Eaton children grew up to become leaders in the affairs of the Connecticut colony.

The strange appearance of the specter of Mr. Lamberton's ship and its subsequent disappearance were said to have been witnessed by many people. The story created a stir in the colonies, and in several cases it was described in letters written by distinguished correspondents of that period.

Tom Walker and the Devil

About one hundred years after the founding of Charlestown in Massachusetts, there lived in that town a miserly, miserable fellow by the name of Thomas Walker. He was small of stature, nearly all bones and gristle, and possessed a shrill, high voice suggestive of a Banshee. His wizened face was garnished with a persimmon mouth, a thin pointed nose and large, shoe-horn-shaped ears. The main object of his existence was the accumulation of money, and he cared not whether it was obtained by fair means or foul. He would cheat or steal from the Devil himself, providing there was little risk in so doing.

Mean and contemptible as Tom Walker was, he could not hold a candle to his wife. She was a huge, granite-jawed, gimlet-eyed creature, irascible and voluble, who had never been known to perform a kind deed or to have spoken a pleasant word. She frightened children, argued with everyone she met, and was said to have stolen ha'pennies from the eyes of a dead man. Much of her time was spent in efforts to cheat or steal from her spouse, which produced endless quarrels and bickering in their cheerless household.

The couple lived in a meager shanty, thatched with a sod roof and situated like a lonely waif at a distance from the clustered houses of the town. Their reputation was such that

131

only fools or strangers dared to stop at their door. Here they lived, unloved and disharmoniously, until fate . . .

One day Tom Walker journeyed to a beach, some distance from his home, to dig a basket of clams. The afternoon was far advanced by the time he finished his chores. Rather than be overtaken by darkness on an unfamiliar road, he decided to take a short cut.

The path he took led through a dismal swamp, overgrown with brush and briars, the home of water snakes, frogs and owls. The path itself was a succession of old, crumbling logs laid end to end, spanning green slimy pools, malodorous with the smell of rotten vegetation and swamp gases. The basket of clams was heavy, the logs slippery. Tom Walker bumbled along, cursing the impulse which had led him to take such a wretched path.

At last he reached a large island in the middle of the swamp. It had once been a refuge for Indians during the deadly strife of King Phillip's War. In this dank retreat, arbored by giant oaks and beeches, captured colonists had been tortured and murdered by the vengeful savages. More than one death shriek had echoed through these somber glades. A company of Boston soldiers, led by a drunken native, surrounded the place near the end of the war and killed the Indians without mercy. Since that bloody day, the island had been shunned because of its evil history.

Tom Walker was a hardened reprobate, so the place held no terror for him. Setting his basket of clams on the ground, he sat down on a fallen tree to rest. Suddenly he was startled by a hard clap on his shoulder that nearly pitched him on his face. A deep voice said, "Welcome, Tom Walker."

Tom glanced around and beheld a huge man, dressed in dirty buckskin, torn black stockings, pewter-buckled shoes and a rusty cocked hat. His skin was coffee-colored, covered with bumps, moles and pox scars. In his hands was a double-bitted axe.

"You're an odd-looking swab," Tom commented ill-naturedly. "Who the Devil are you?"

The stranger chuckled. "You called the turn. I *am* the Devil. Through many centuries I have been known by such names as Satan, Lucifer, Beelzebub, Mephisto, Old Nick, Old Scratch and Old Ned. In this country I would prefer to be known as the Black Woodsman."

"Harumph!" Tom snorted. "Maybe I am not as smart as one of the King's magistrates; nevertheless, you can't take me in with such nonsensical claims." His eyes narrowed slyly. "I've been told that the Devil can turn dross into gold." Reaching into his pocket, Tom pulled out a handful of dried beans which he had gleaned from a farmer's garden. "If ye are truly Old Scratch, then turn these beans into gold."

The self-styled Black Woodsman glared angrily at Tom Walker. "So you must have proof," he snarled. "Very well! Look at your beans."

Tom's eyes widened in surprise. The beans in his hand had turned into gold. Avariciously he cuddled the gold beans in his hand while he glanced suspiciously at his companion.

"I take it that you like gold," the Devil said with a chuckle.

"Aye! I do. There is not much I wouldn't do to get a hatful," Tom answered truthfully.

The Fiend looked pleased. "Perhaps I can put you in the way of getting some. Several years ago my old subject, Captain Kidd, the pirate, buried a rich treasure on a hillock near the Saugus River. Kidd is now swinging from a gibbet, so he has no more need for it. If you will sign a contract to give me your body and soul when you die, I will show you where to dig for Kidd's gold. There is more than a hatful."

"Aye! I will sign—providing that you promise to take no action to lessen my life's span."

"Agreed," the Devil said. "I shall wait until you call me."

Taking a parchment from his pocket, he drew up a contract and Tom Walker signed it. It was late when Tom arrived home that night. No sooner had he entered the house than his wife set at him. She would know where he had been, what he had been doing, whom he had robbed or cheated, and how much money he had acquired.

Tom refused to talk. His refusal provoked a quarrel, and soon the couple were screaming and cursing at each other like inmates of Bedlam. Finally, worn out by the verbal affray, Tom proceeded to tell his wife of all that had befallen him that day. This confession only engendered further recriminations.

"What a stupid you are," she railed. "You sell yourself for a chest of gold you have never seen. How can you trust the Devil? Captain Kidd's treasure! Fiddlesticks! If you had had sense enough to bargain with him, you might have returned home with enough gold to make us both rich. You are a fool. Tomorrow I shall go to the island in the swamp. I'll warrant that I will drive a sharp bargain with the Old Fiend."

The following morning Dame Walker set out to find the Devil. She was never seen again. A hunter later found her shawl floating on the surface of a deep pool in the swamp.

Tom Walker spent little time mourning for his scrapmate. Within a fortnight after her disappearance he sold the house and land and left Charlestown.

Some time later an affluent Thomas Walker arrived in Boston. Hiring a small room, he set up a loan office. Hard money was scarce, so many well-to-do merchants and artisans, as well as people of small means, were forced by hard times to patronize his business. Freely he loaned money to them at usurious rates. Those unfortunates who found themselves unable to pay received no sympathy or mercy. He squeezed the poor souls dry, taking from them everything of value—even to the clothing on their back.

Thus, in a short time Tom Walker became very wealthy. However, lifetime habits are difficult to change. Despite his wealth he was greedy for more. His niggardliness kept him from spending and enjoying his money.

As he grew older and richer, he became obsessed with a fear of being robbed. He commissioned a blacksmith to build a large iron strongbox, bound with iron straps and safeguarded by three brass locks. In this safe he kept his gold and business papers.

About this time his pact with the Black Woodsman must have been preying on his mind. He began to carry a Bible in his pocket. He even joined the congregation of a church, figuring, no doubt, that in this way he would cheat the Devil. Hypocritically he mouthed religious phrases on Sundays and skinned the hides from his debtors the balance of the week.

One hot afternoon Tom was busy in his office, scanning a list of mortgages. Perspiring freely he finally took off his coat and draped it over a chair. An old man entered the office, rubbing his hands together nervously, his rheumy eyes blinking at Walker.

"I have come here to ask a favor of you," he piped. "I cannot raise the money for the mortgage payments on my house. I would like you to wait until my son comes home. He will pay you. He is a sailor and owns his own ship."

"Damn your impudence," Tom snarled. "I'll foreclose. I would rather let the 'Old Fiend' take me than to give you one hour over your bounden time."

At that moment the doorway was darkened by the entrance of a smoky colored giant, dressed in frayed buckskin. "I've come for you, Tom Walker," he said.

Tom jumped up in alarm and tried to reach the Bible in his coat pocket, but he was too late. The stranger grabbed him by the scruff of his skinny neck and dragged him from the room.

A frightened clerk said later that he saw Tom Walker and the man in buckskin mounted on a black horse, galloping like the Devil toward Charlestown. He also claimed that smoke and blue flames issued from the horse's mouth. This last intelligence, however, was discredited by the authorities.

Walker was never seen again, and only a cursory search was ever made for him. In the process of time his large iron chest was opened under the watchful eyes of a magistrate. It was found to contain nothing more valuable than a peck of charred papers and a dozen sacks filled with stones.

It has been said that several hunters in afteryears claimed to have seen a weathered slate gravestone on the island in the swamp. Engraved on it was this short epitaph: Thomas Walker. Born April 1, 1680. Went to Hell in the year 1739.

General Moulton's Boot

Jonathan Moulton of Hampton, New Hampshire, was a tough man. In a frontier settlement where courage was taken for granted, where every man faced death daily from marauding Indians and wild beasts, Jonathan gained renown as the bravest, fightingest, most cantankerous man in the whole region. He also possessed another kind of reputation. His neighbors described him as a master of rascality and sharp practices, who would cheat the Devil if given the opportunity.

In his youth Jonathan resided in Boston. Being a knave at heart, and not too religious-minded, he incurred the displeasure of the Puritan authorities, who suggested with some force that he would be wise to leave the vicinity. He removed to Salem but stayed there only for a short time before moving on. Sometime later he arrived in Hampton, which at that time was a frontier wilderness, cleared a plot of land and built a cabin. Within a year he was trading with the local Indians. He cheated them, stole their land and drove them away. When they became angry and began to retaliate, he led a company of settlers against them. With gun and sword the Englishmen slaughtered them. The few Indians who managed to escape left their lands and moved into the mountains.

Jonathan sold the Indian lands, cheated his neighbors, built a fine house and prospered. In the French and Indian War, he led a company of Hampton men to Louisburg to fight the French. His courage and lack of principles brought him rapid advancement. Before the fall of the fortress he had been promoted to the rank of general.

When he returned from the war, General Jonathan Moulton settled in his new home, married a local girl and began to cast around for ways to make money. However, it was not easy. He had killed off the Indians, and his neighbors had grown wary of his methods and refused to have any business dealings with him.

Sitting in front of his fireplace one evening, Jonathan decried the lack of opportunities to get rich. "Must I scrabble eternally to gain a small living?" he asked aloud. "I would do *anything* to become wealthy. Why, I would sell my soul to the Devil for a boot full of gold."

Suddenly a shower of sparks flew down the chimney, and a puff of smoke momentarily blinded him. He coughed and wiped his eyes, then started in surprise. Standing in front of the fireplace was a sharp-featured stranger, richly dressed in black velvet.

"This is a business call," the stranger said, "so let's at it. I have business with Governor Wentworth at Portsmouth in fifteen minutes. Now let's see! You expressed a wish to sell your soul for a boot full of gold. Is that correct?"

"Yearly," the general amended.

"Fair enough! A boot full every year."

The stranger took from his pocket a most impressive looking document and laid it on the table. "Sign here!" he commanded.

"Not so fast!" Jonathan protested. "First, although I presume you are the Devil, I would have you say so. Second, how do I know that you can or will fulfill your part of the bargain?"

The stranger waved one hand airily. "I have been called many names. What is in a name? Salt, call it what you wish, will still be salt and possess the same savor. If you feel better for it, you may call me Satan. Now for the second part of your protest." He shook his head and a dozen gold coins cascaded from his wig and fell to the floor.

Gold! Beautiful gold! Jonathan fell to his knees and picked up a shiny gold sovereign only to drop it quickly. It was red hot.

"Wait until they cool," Satan cautioned him. "Remember, they came from a pretty warm place."

Impatiently the general waited, his eyes fixed on the bright gold pieces. Finally the devil nodded and Jonathan gingerly picked up one. It was cool. Hastily he scrambled over the floor, picking up the rest of the coins. How persuasive they were. Taking his quill pen and ink from the mantel, he signed the devil's document. Even in the act of scratching his name on the paper, he was busily mulling over plans to cheat his new partner.

"My boots are not fit to hold gold," he told Satan. "Wait until the morrow. I will buy a new pair and leave one boot hanging on the fireplace wall. I will expect you to fill it with gold pieces."

"Agreed. Now we should drink a toast to seal our bargain. Have you any rum in the house? I like rum. It is a drink for wild and lusty fellows."

In the Moulton kitchen was a jug of "rot gut" rum. Good enough for the Devil, Jonathan thought. He filled two drinking horns with the potent liquor. Stirring a large pinch of snuff in one of them, he offered it to Satan.

"Here's to a warm friendship," that gentleman said. Raising his drinking horn, he emptied the contents down his gullet in one deep draught.

"This is uncommonly fine rum," he praised.

Setting the drinking horn on the mantel, the Devil gave a low whistle. Instantly a thick cloud of smoke issued from the fireplace and enveloped him. When it thinned out, Satan had disappeared.

The next day Jonathan went shopping for boots. He finally bought a pair of huge trooper's jackboots which reached to the hip. One of these he hung on the chimney wall.

The Devil was surprised at the size of the boot, but a bargain is a bargain, so he filled it to the brim with bright gold sovereigns and continued to do so once every year.

Thus General Jonathan Moulton became extremely wealthy. He added seven rooms to his house, hired servants, bought a carriage and gave his wife jewels worth a fortune. He had everything money could buy, yet he could not stop cheating.

One day the Devil arrived at the Moulton house on his annual visit. According to the agreement, he began to pour gold pieces into the large boot. A flood of gold coins poured into the leathern receptacle but the boot did not fill up. Perplexed, Satan pulled the boot from the wall. In the sole was a large hole which had butted up against a hole in the fireplace wall. The gold coins had been pouring from the boot into the chimney and from there to the cellar. The devil shook his head sorrowfully at such a perfidious act and left the house. That night the Moulton house burned to the ground. Mrs. Moulton and the general barely escaped with their lives.

Most of the gold received from the Devil had been hidden in the house, and Jonathan felt sure that it could be recovered. After the embers cooled, he began to search through the burned rubble, but strange to relate, not one piece of gold was ever found in the ruins.

Another legend concerning General Moulton relates that sometime after the Moulton house burned, his wife died. Jonathan gave her a fine funeral, but within a few weeks of her demise he married a lovely young girl only half his age.

On their wedding night the amorous general gave his new bride a ring and a costly necklace which had belonged to his first wife. Early the next morning the girl bride awoke. Beside her the general lay sleeping deeply. Suddenly she saw a woman dressed in a long, flowing robe and carrying a lighted candle approaching her. Walking to the bed, the intruder glared down at the panic-stricken girl.

"The jewels are mine. You shall not have them," the woman said. Roughly she pulled the ring from the bride's finger and snatched the necklace from her bosom.

Terrified screams from his new wife awoke the general. For a long time the girl was incoherent, unable to give any reason for her abject terror. It was dawn before she was able to tell of the nocturnal visitor and the loss of the jewels. The house and grounds were searched, but the ring and necklace were never found. Neighbors who heard of the incident were inclined to believe that the intruder was the ghost of the first Mrs. Moulton. They believed that she had left her grave to take her love gifts from her youthful successor.

Several years later General Jonathan Moulton died and was interred in a heavy slate coffin. Months went by. Then a rumor became prevalent that the general's coffin was filled with gold coins. Curious officials prevailed on his widow to have the grave opened. A dozen men went to the graveyard and dug up the coffin. When the lid was pried off, the coffin was found to be empty. There was neither gold nor corpse. This confirmed the opinion of many that the Devil had claimed his own.

The Devil's Bride

A story of Old Salisbury, Massachusetts, tells of a somewhat disreputable woman who was seen carrying an earthen jug into a barn. Shortly thereafter a tall, dark man was observed entering the same building.

The owner of the barn was delayed in investigating these unusual visitations by a sudden, violent storm which shook the countryside with frequent claps of thunder. When the farmer finally entered his barn, he could find no signs of the dark man. However, he found the woman laying in a coma on the hay.

When revived, she said that Old Beelzebub had pursued her into the barn and frightened her quite out of her wits. He had charmed her into an agreement to sell him her body and soul, binding the bargain with three drops of blood drawn from her forefinger. He then said that she was his bride and told her to get ready for a honeymoon. In six days, on the stroke of ten o'clock in the morning, he would come to claim her as his own.

The farmer was somewhat skeptical of her tale, especially after finding her earthen jug in the hay smelling strongly of rum. Good Parson Seales of Old Salisbury, however, believed her story and determined to save her from the Devil. He asked twelve brother clergymen from neighboring towns to assist him.

On the day appointed by the Devil, a large crowd assembled in farmer Pettinghill's orchard. Many of them were curious to see what the Old Fiend looked like. They gave the woman a good stiff drink of rum and tied her securely in a chair. The clergymen formed a circle around her. Seales strengthened the fortifications by placing deacons and church members three-deep surrounding the men of the pulpit.

As the appointed hour drew near, they began to pray and sing hymns. A black cat leaped down from an apple tree, spitting and squalling, setting everyone's nerves on edge. A strong odor of brimstone permeated the air. The chair with the trussed-up "Devil's Bride" rocked violently back and forth. Deacon Smith received a sharp blow on his buttocks, which drew from him an uncanny scream, and Mother Pettinghill's skirts were pulled up over her head by a strange force, showing an unholy expanse of bare flesh. The brave clergymen, despite these manifestations, continued to pray and the violence ceased. The Devil had been overcome.

Parson Seales was right proud of his successful encounter with Old Nick—as he had a right to be. The woman whom he had saved attended services at his meetinghouse for three weeks, speaking often with gratitude of Mr. Seales's "great faith and courage."

The entire congregation was shocked one Sunday morning when her body was found in Deacon Smith's well. The verdict of the town constable, who fished her body from the well, was that she had come to her death accidentally. An empty jug of rum beside the well was considered circumstantial evidence.

Her remains were given a Christian burial without anyone even hinting that the Devil had won out in the end.

Lady Eleanore's Mantle

This is a tale of pride and beauty, of an all-consuming passion, and rumors of witchcraft and the Devil's work.

In the early colonial days, when the Bay Colony of Massachusetts was still a lusty young offspring of Old England, a famous beauty, Lady Eleanore Rochcliffe, ruled over the aristocratic salons in London. She was so beautiful that men willingly gave up their fortunes, their careers, even gave up their families, to compete for her favors. Several men dueled to the death over her. Two men, maddened by their unrequited love for Eleanore, killed themselves. Outwardly she appeared to be a sweet and tender woman, but inwardly the Lady Eleanore was cold, arrogant and cruel.

Although men were attracted by her beauty, women were repelled. There were rumors—rumors that her loveliness was the handiwork of the Devil, to whom she was beholden. There were also rumors concerning a mantle which she often wore. This mantle was reputed to have been sewn together by witches. The possessor of this magical garment would always appear young and beautiful.

Among the scores of London gallants who courted Lady Eleanore was a young man named Gervase Helwyse, who was said to be of good family. His mad passion for Eleanore induced him to squander his fortune while attempting to gain her favor. His estates and personal possessions were sold to finance his pursuit. There came a day when he had not a shilling that he could call his own. Without money he was no longer welcome in the salons of the wealthy which the Lady Rochcliffe frequented. His passion for Eleanore finally drove him mad. Everywhere she went in public he followed, pleading his love. One evening he forced his way into her house. Angered by his persistence, she had her servants whip him from the premises. Thereafter he disappeared.

The beauty's round of self-seeking pleasure came to an end when her grandfather died, leaving extensive estates. The King appointed her cousin, Sir Samuel Shute, as her guardian. At that time Shute was in far-off Boston, serving as royal governor of the Massachusetts province. On a sudden caprice Lady Eleanore decided to visit her guardian. She sent a letter to him acquainting him with her plans. A short time later, she boarded a ship bound for New England. When Governor Shute received his cousin's letter, he quickly made plans to entertain her.

News of the coming arrival of the famous London beauty caused a stir in the colony. This promised to be a social event of the first magnitude. The governor had already announced that he would give a ball in honor of his ward, so the ladies at once began to refurbish their wardrobes.

Finally the awaited day arrived. The *Bounty of London* anchored in the harbor, and the governor boarded the ship to greet his famous cousin. Crowds watched as the pair landed and entered the governor's splendid coach. Hundreds of citizens along the streets cheered them as the carriage drove to the Province House, where the governor resided.

As the Lady Eleanore was about to alight from the conveyance, a pale, disheveled young man pushed through the crowd of spectators and fell at her feet, offering himself as a footstool for her to step on. It was Gervase Helwyse.

"Get out of here, you rascal," the governor shouted, striking at the youth with his cane.

Lady Rochcliffe interceded. "Do not strike him. When men wish to be trampled, it is a favor they deserve."

Her pretty face a picture of scorn, she stepped on the recumbent man and thence to the ground. Tucking her hand under His Excellency's arm, she walked majestically into the Province House.

Several evenings later, a brilliant ball in honor of Lady Eleanore Rochcliffe was held in the governor's mansion. Most of the socially prominent families of Massachusetts were there. The beautiful hostess, richly dressed and jeweled, moved through the crowded ballroom, accepting greetings and acknowledging introductions. She was followed by a train of male admirers. She wore her mantle, which evoked much interest. Rumors of its origin had followed her to New England.

While the guests were taking refreshments, Gervase Helwyse entered the ballroom. He pushed rudely through the circle of Eleanore's admirers and knelt before her, holding out to her a goblet of wine. As she hesitated, a young man struck the goblet to the floor.

"Is it poison? Do you dare to poison our lady?" the young man asked.

"No! It was wine," Gervase said, as the men jostled around him.

"Pray, gentlemen, do not hurt my poor admirer," the lady pleaded languorously.

Suddenly Gervase leaped forward and pulled the mantle from Lady Eleanore's shoulders. He tried to cast it into the fireplace, but several men intercepted him, took away the mantle and forced him out of the ballroom. With ejaculations of indignation against the mad young man, the mantle was returned to its owner.

Thereafter, Lady Eleanore, her face flushed, her speech erratic and faltering, continued to dance and mingle with the guests. After a lively cotillion, she complained of dizziness, and the governor summoned Dr. Clarke to examine her. The good doctor looked searchingly at the beauty's flushed face and dilated eyes.

"The lady is ill. If what I suspect is true, she will be very sick. I would suggest that the entertainment be stopped at once."

"But why?" asked the governor.

The doctor said a few words in a low voice and His Excellency started in alarm. An announcement was made to the guests that due to unforeseen circumstances it was necessary to end the ball quickly. By the following morning it was known that Lady Rochcliffe had been stricken with the pox.

For two weeks the beautiful Eleanore lay in a darkened room in the Province House fighting for her life, and she was not alone. Many of the people who had attended the ball also contracted the disease. Within a short time a terrible smallpox epidemic was raging in the city. Hundreds of houses flew the red plague flags in front of their doors. Hundreds of people died and were buried in long pits, their bodies covered with lime.

Lady Eleanore passed the crisis and lived. She lived—but never again would she be the toast of London. Her once beautiful face had been made hideous by pockmarks and an incrustation of scabs. She hid in a darkened room, half-demented, moaning against the loathsome disease which had robbed her of her most prized possession. She was alone. The governor and his servants had fled. She was alone with the ashes of her pride and the remembrance of her conceit.

One day Gervase Helwyse entered the governor's mansion.

There was no one to challenge him. Muttering madly he searched the house. He came to a room, a room shuttered and dark. From somewhere in the darkness came muted sobs. Feeling his way to the window, Gervase opened the shutters, flooding the room with light. He turned to see a piteous sight. On a bed, discolored from the excretions of numerous pox sores, cowered a woman. Her blonde, unkept hair framed a countenance terribly disfigured by the disease.

"Who are you?" Helwyse demanded.

The woman wailed thinly. Even her vocal cords had been affected by her illness.

"Please help me," she pleaded. "I am Lady Eleanore Rochcliffe."

Gervase Helwyse stood near the window, rocking back and forth on his heels, wild laughter bubbling in his throat.

"You? You claim you are Lady Eleanore?"

His mad mirth threatened to choke him.

"Do not lie! The Lady Eleanore is the loveliest creature in all the world. You—you are a witch, a foul witch."

Still laughing, he snatched her fabled mantle from a chair and ran from the house.

On the Common, a great pyre was sending smoke and flames high in the air. The clothing, bedding and many of the possessions of victims of the plague were being burned, watched by hundreds of people. Suddenly the onlookers screamed in horror. A madman, waving a richly trimmed mantle, leaped into the flames.

From that moment the plague abated. Within the year it had become naught but a sad memory. Hundreds had died. A few recovered. Yet the most tragic of the survivors was the disfigured, unwanted, unloved creature who haunted the shadows of Province House, the once famous beauty, Lady Eleanore Rochcliffe.

Legend of the Witch of Cape Ann

Old Governor Shirley of Massachusetts became angry at the French for buying English scalps from the Indians and pirating colonial shipping with their Canada-based privateers. Therefore, in the spring of 1745 he began to raise an army of colonial militia to give the Frenchies in Canada a taste of English powder. His grandiose plan was to capture the great fortress of Louisburg.

The colonists responded with enthusiam. Reckless young devils from towns, farms and fishing hamlets were quick to "jine up." A war was more to their liking than serving apprenticeships, grubbing in corn fields or salting and drying codfish.

On Cape Ann the boys formed a company, elected officers and began to drill in the meadow behind the Old Towne Tavern, where refreshments were available for thirsty soldiers. War was a lark. Everyone was healthy and happy until the witch of Cape Ann laid a curse on them. Then trouble began.

Cape Ann at that time possessed, or was possesed by, a real, honest-to-goodness witch named Meg Wesson. Contemporary accounts picture her as a hunchbacked crone with a wrinkled face, hooked nose, yellow eyes and a bird's nest of stringy gray hair. She lived in a ramshackled sod house on a low hill overlooking the salt marshes near the Annisquam

River. With her were her pets—a huge black cat, a hissing, evil-tempered goose and a thieving, one-eyed raven. The inhabitants of the Cape gave her home a wide berth, although somewhat perversely they were proud of her infamous reputation. Her rumored actions and misdeeds provided choice morsels of conversation among the superstitious country folk.

It was said that she had only to pass a farmhouse, and the milk would sour, the hens stop laying, and the babies wake up with the colic. Every misadventure suffered by the people on the Cape was blamed on her. The two-headed calf born to Andy Sargent's brindle cow, the frequent fits of little Tommy Starr, the conflagration which destroyed Morris Simes's boat, even the collapse of Brad Allen's outhouse which left Millicent Allen in a very embarrassing position were blamed on spells cast by Old Meg.

One day shortly before the Cape Ann militia embarked for Canada, Old Meg Wesson arrived at the tavern with a mess of eels to trade for a bottle of rum. A group of militiamen, several of them tipsy, were in the taproom drinking a potent blend of hard cider and rum. Brave from the spirits within, they began to test the sharpness of their humor on the old hag.

"Come on, Old Bag of Bones," Ben Josslyn roared, "give us a charm to enchant the French girls in Canady."

"Where is your broomstick?" young Tom Day asked with a maudlin laugh.

Angered by their impudence, Old Meg pointed a shaking, gnarled finger at them.

"Young fools," she hissed, "may ye be cursed by water, by land and by air. May maggots and worms consume thy bodies and may birds nest in your sun-bleached skulls. Ye want a charm? Here be one."

She tossed a live eel on the floor. Later, her frightened audience claimed that the eel slithered across the floor and into the fireplace where it burned like a wax taper.

"Trouble and suffering from this day on—that is what ye will receive."

Muttering direfully, the old woman left the tavern, leaving the young soldiers somewhat crestfallen and sober.

The witch's curse became effective almost at once. That very evening, Ben Josslyn shot himself in the foot while cleaning his gun and had to be carried to his mother's house in Gloucester. One week later, while the company was embarking on the transport *Lucky Lass*, Tom Day fell overboard and injured his head on a piling. Misfortune dogged the *Lucky Lass* and her Cape Ann passengers as they sailed in a large convoy toward Canada. The drinking water became foul, the wind blew from the wrong quarter, and twice the ship ran aground, causing irritating delays.

When the Cape Ann militia landed at Gabarus Bay, their bad luck only took a turn for the worse. They were ordered to build roads and haul cannon across hip-deep swamps toward the invested town of Louisburg. Day after day they toiled at their backbreaking tasks. Dysentery, fevers and chickenpox took their toll of the company. As they advanced toward the French fortifications, bullets and cannon ball further decimated their ranks. Every day they were forced to endure the bite of gnats, the sting of mosquitoes and the raucous caw of a huge raven which flew over their company.

It was Amos Allen who first suggested that the black bird of evil omen might be the old witch, Meg Wesson. This idea received ready credence and occasioned a council of war. After a discussion, the members of the Cape Ann company decided to mold two silver bullets (for only silver bullets can harm a witch) and commissioned John Stout and Arthur King, their finest marksmen, to shoot the raven.

The following day when the raven flew over their position, John Stout and Arthur King fired at the bird. A cheer went up from the company as it fluttered and fell to earth. Examination showed that one of the bullets had broken the raven's leg, the other had penetrated its body. It was dead.

The Cape Ann boys were elated, certain that Meg Wesson's spell over them had been broken. Circumstances aided their belief. Two days after the death of the raven, the great fortress of Louisburg surrendered.

When the Cape Ann company returned home, they were informed of an amazing and incredible event. On the date and the exact hour that Stout and King had shot the raven, Meg Wesson had screamed and fallen to the ground near the river road. One of her legs had been broken. Dr. Proctor was called to the scene but found the old woman dead on his arrival.

When the witch's body was being prepared for burial, two silver bullets fell from her clothing.

Curse of the Abenaki

For fifty years French-sponsored war parties from the Indian town of St. Francis in Canada had traveled wilderness trails to attack lonely English settlements in the Hampshire Grants, in Massachusetts and New Hampshire. Hardly a family on the frontier had not suffered the loss of loved ones at the hands of these marauders. For fifty years these savage sorties had stirred anger, engendered hatred and thoughts of revenge. Every English settler believed that someday their cruel foe would harvest a holocaust of revenge for the seeds of hatred which they had been sowing for so long a time. Meanwhile they waited.

Then the St. Francis Indians captured two English officers who were traveling under a flag of truce for Lord Jeffrey Amherst, commander of British troops stationed at Fort Ticonderoga and Crown Point.

When the general learned of this action, he immediately ordered Major Robert Rogers to attack and destroy the Indian town of St. Francis. That same night, the major set out with two hundred of his New England Rangers. The date was September 13, 1759.

The St. Francis Indians were having a high time on the evening of October 5. There had been a wedding, and the entire populace was participating in the celebration. Merriment pre-

153

vailed despite an old medicine man's prediction that a dreadful calamity would soon be visited on the Abenaki tribe, which composed more than 75 per cent of the population of the town. Finally, in the early hours of morning, the wedding festivities ceased. Gates in the cedar log stockade which enclosed the place were closed but left unguarded. Quickly the tired celebrators succumbed to sleep. Even the usually restless Indian dogs slumbered. The campfires burned to ashes. The buildings and lodges were enveloped in darkness. Hours passed. A faint tinge of pink on the horizon presaged the coming of morning.

Then, like disembodied spirits, a file of dark figures emerged from the forest. Some of them ran along the banks of the river, slashing holes through the sides of beached canoes. A large group asembled near the stockade. Figures climbed the log walls and dropped within the enclosure. Quietly they swung open the gates. Major Robert Roger's Rangers had gained their objective.

Hurriedly they checked their weapons. A soft spoken command and they raced toward the rows of silent wigwams, cabins, and the framed mission church of St. Francois de Sales. Torches were lit and tossed into doorways. Shrill screams and war whoops, punctuated by the staccato crackling of gunfire, aroused the town. Shrieking natives ran frantically toward the river in an attempt to escape. They pushed the damaged canoes into the river and leaped aboard only to have their frail craft founder under them. A score of the Rangers stood on the river's edge shooting at the defenseless Indians in the water. These men were fine marksmen. Nearly every shot they fired claimed a victim.

In the streets of the town the conflagration of burning wigwams lighted up long poles stuck into the ground. The poles were decorated with dozens of English scalps, some of them from women.

The sight of these grim tokens of Indian savagery drove the

New Englanders mad. With gun, tomahawk and knife, they butchered the Indians without mercy. Some of the natives fled to the church for protection, pursued by a dozen Rangers. Before the lighted altar stood Father Roubaud, a Jesuit priest, his arms raised in prayer. The frightened Indians scurried behind him and crouched on the floor. A buckskin-clad figure raised his rifle and fired. Father Roubaud fell dead without a sound. Leaping over his body, the Rangers clubbed the natives with their rifle butts. Pausing to gaze at their bloody handiwork, they heard a sepulchral voice coming from the pile of battered bodies before the altar.

"Listen ye," the voice intoned, "the Great Spirit of the Abenaki will scatter darkness in the paths of the accursed English palefaces! Hunger walks before—and death strikes their trails! Their squaws weep for the warriors that do not return! Manitou is angry when the dead speak. The dead have spoken!"

The Rangers hastily ransacked the church and, after setting fire to it, carried away a golden chalice, two heavy gold candlesticks, a cross and a large silver statue of the Madonna. As leaping flames consumed the church, a bell in the steeple began to toll slowly as if the hands of the dead were sounding their own requiem. Over two hundred Indians were killed, and every house and wigwam was burned by the New Englanders, but many of the St. Francis warriors escaped.

Major Rogers realized that the angry Abenaki would reorganize their forces and pursue his column. He had already decided to retreat by forced marches along the Yamaska River to Lake Memphremagog and thence east to the Connecticut River settlements. While the town of St. Francis was still burning, he reassembled his raiders and ordered them to be ready to march at a moment's notice. He pictured to them the long miles of wilderness trails they would have to traverse before the English settlements were reached. "Food is essential," he told them. "Our supplies are depleted. Search the town for every scrap of food you can find. Fill your knapsacks with food. Carry nothing else. This is a matter of life or death."

Unfortunately cupidity overcame their good sense. Many of the Rangers filled their knapsacks with plunder while large amounts of food were allowed to burn.

Two hours after the attack had begun, the New Englanders left the smoking ruins of the Indian town and marched along an ill-defined trail toward the Yamaska River. With them were five Indian prisoners and five rescued English captives. Their route crossed rivers, swamps and a maze of rocky gorges and ravines. Several times they lost their way and spent precious time finding the right trails. Rain and snow bedeviled them. Before they reached the shores of Lake Memphremagog the specter of starvation faced them. A small store of parched corn was rationed, but it did little to assuage their hunger.

When the column reached the lake, Major Rogers held a council of war. The pursuing Indians were a deadly menace. Only by continued swift marches could the Rangers expect to escape. However, the lack of food was weakening the men and slowing down the column. It would only be a matter of time before the vengeful savages would catch up with them. Yet it was imperative that meat should be procured as quickly as possible. In this dilemma the Rangers decided to break up the column into seven units, each in the charge of an officer. The groups would separate and hunt in different directions, taking every precaution to avoid ambush by their pursuers. All parties would head for the Connecticut River where they were to wait for supplies to be sent to them from Number Four, the northernmost fort in the Hampshire Grants.

From that day on, the grim curse of the Abenakis began to decimate the desperate bands of Rangers. Fish and game were virtually nonexistent. Two hunting parties stumbled into Indian ambushes and were wiped out. Stragglers died of starvation or were tracked down and slain by the St. Francis warriors. Heavy snows and bitter cold weather added to their woes.

Major Rogers with several of the strongest Rangers traveled doggedly to the banks of the Connecticut River. A raft was built and the major, with one of his men, poled the craft down the river toward Number Four. The raft was wrecked in a series of rapids. After incredible hardships, Major Rogers and his companion reached the settlements and sent rescue teams laden with food up the river to save the remnants of his Ranger companies.

One of the Ranger groups, heavily laden with loot from the Church of St. Francois, was fortunate in evading the Indian trackers. This party, accompanied by two captive Indian squaws, was commanded by a British captain who had been attached to the Ranger command by Lord Amherst. The captain had been badly wounded in the attack on St. Francis, but he refused to allow his condition to slow up the group. He forced himself by sheer grit to set a fast pace. Every evening after the day's march, one of the squaws, a comely young Abenaki, tenderly cleansed his wounds and bound them with compresses of shredded herbs.

The knowledge of the captive squaws saved this party from dying of starvation. They found patches of wild onions and other edible bulbs along the route of march. They boiled these with moss and lichen, making an evil-looking but nourishing stew. However, other troubles beset this group.

Amos Parsons, a huge, surly, dark-visaged Hampshireman, one of the Ranger veterans, truculently refused to obey the captain's commands. He attempted to persuade others in the party to mutiny against the Englishman. He met with some success. Nine of the Rangers accepted his leadership.

When this party reached the Connecticut River, the captain announced his intentions to descend the river to Number Four. Parsons protested violently, urging his comrades to follow him across the highlands to the White Mountain passes and the settlements beyond. Confronted by this insubordination, the British captain raised his musket and aimed it at Parsons's head.

"Sergeant Parsons! You have the choice of two courses," he said grimly. "Either you follow and obey my orders—or we shall bury you here. Which way do you want it?"

The suddenly subdued Ranger capitulated and promised to obey the captain's further commands. Later that same night, however, while the captain slept, the nine mutineers stealthily opened the packs of their sleeping companions and stole the St. Francis loot with everything else of value. They gagged the two Indian women so they could not awake the camp and led them toward the river. By the wan light of a frosty moon, they crossed the icy Connecticut and followed an Indian trail toward the White Mountains.

The first rays of the rising sun were painting the treetops with gold when Amos Parsons called a halt. The men stacked their muskets and began to gather wood for a fire. One of them stopped in front of the Indian women who squatted dispiritedly by the side of the trail. He touched the younger squaw on the shoulder. With the speed of a striking snake, she pulled a knife from her clothing and stabbed him in the throat. Before his stunned companions could move, she dashed into the woods. Two of the men followed her but she eluded them.

The wounded Ranger died soon after, and the mutineers, unable to dig a grave in the frozen ground, covered his body with brush and stones. Then, filled with a sense of foreboding by the tragic death of their comrade, they continued toward the White Mountains.

The stabbing affair seemed to have unhinged the mind of Amos Parsons. He heaped indignities on his remaining captive, forcing her to carry his heavy knapsack and camp gear. At the slightest excuse he beat her unmercifully. If one of the Rangers remonstrated, he would curse him and threaten to kill anyone who might dare to oppose his actions.

Staggering through deepening snow and bitter cold, the small party suffered worsening pangs of hunger. The Indian squaw refused to search for food, even though her refusal brought instant, brutal beatings from the irascible Amos Parsons. She did, however, promise to guide them through the mountain passes.

Seeking vengeance for all the evil which had befallen her, the Indian woman led the party into the labyrinth of rocky clefts and valleys that compose the Israel River region of the White Mountains.

Food was nonexistent. The small group of Rangers became progressively weaker every day. One man became insane and attacked his companions with fingernails and teeth. The struggle to subdue him expended the little remaining energy left in their starved bodies. Like ragged, limp manikins, they huddled in a rocky defile, unable to go on, waiting for death to release them from their misery.

The wind, whipping snow over their freezing bodies, aroused Amos Parsons from a stupor. Slowly he stood erect and staggered to a cleft in the rock where the squaw had burrowed a hole in the snow. Taking her hand, he pulled her from the snow shelter. Weakly, the pair leaned together for a moment, then, like two drunkards, they staggered away through the snow, leaving their freezing companions. Behind them, a snow-covered form moved. The insane Ranger, his eyes pools of madness, struggled to his feet. Laughing crazily he followed the two.

The Indian woman led Amos to a cave and somehow contrived to build a fire. The heat revived the sergeant's waning vitality. He was cold. Even the fire did not warm him—but he was alive. He commanded the squaw to give him her deerskin tunic. When she refused, he struck her and stripped the torn and stained garment from her. Wrapping it around his shoulders and waist, he crouched over the fire. Weakness plucked at his eyelids. Presently he lay back on the rocky floor and slept.

The Indian woman watched the sleeping man, her dark eyes showing no expression. After a while she crept to the farthest extremity of the cave. In the darkness she searched until her hands touched the cold bodies of many hibernating reptiles. She selected a large snake and returned to the fire to examine it. It was a rattlesnake, torpid from the low temperature. Carefully the woman parted the clothing of the sleeping Ranger and placed the cold snake on his chest. Shivering from the cold, she crept close to the fire, her eyes watching the slumbering man with the deadly reptile coiled on his chest.

Time passed. The snake, warmed by the body heat of the Ranger, stirred. The glassy eyes opened. Amos Parsons moved in his sleep. He raised one arm and dropped it on the coiled snake. Lethal fangs sank into his flesh. He opened his eyes and beheld the weaving head of the serpent inches from his face. Gripped in the throes of utter fear, he screamed. While the screams were issuing from his straining throat, the rattlesnake struck again and again.

The screams weakened and died out, and were replaced by cackling laughter from the Indian squaw. Back and forth she rocked on her heels, laughing at the death struggle of Amos Parsons. She happened to glance at the cave entrance and her laughter ended abruptly. Mad eyes stared at her as the crazy Ranger shuffled into the cave.

Two weeks later, a farmer riding into Conway sighted a ragged, hairy man staggering along the road, alternately laughing and crying. On his back was a dirty, stained knapsack. He offered no resistance when the farmer bundled him on a sled and dragged him into town.

In Conway the stranger was taken to a tavern and fed. He

was unquestionably mad. He refused to allow anyone to touch his knapsack, holding it in his lap while he ate. After some discussion he was placed in a barred room. When he went to sleep, several townsmen entered his room and removed the pack. They placed it on a table and unbuckled the straps. Impatiently one of the men lifted the knapsack and shook out its contents on the table. The curious onlookers recoiled in horror. Lying on the table were the bloody, half-eaten arms and legs of a woman.

Through the years, exaggerated tales of the rich loot taken from St. Francis by Rogers's Rangers, most of which was rumored to have been lost or buried, caused many a hunter to search the wilderness for treasure. Most of these treasure seekers confined their search to the valleys and passes in the White Mountains. That the "curse of the Abenaki" was still potent was attested to by the number of treasure hunters who were killed or laid low by unusual accidents.

One old hunter found six rusty gun barrels and a pile of rotted knapsacks in a rocky ravine. Searching further, he discovered a large cave. He made a torch of pine bark, ignited it and entered the cave. A short distance from the entrance, he wandered into a wide chamber. On the rocky floor he saw a skull, seemingly grinning at him. Suddenly and inexplicably, the torch went out. As the old hunter tried to find the entrance in the darkness, his foot slipped on a loose rock and he fell heavily. He felt the smooth surface of the skull beneath his hand. Horrified, he felt sharp teeth gnawing on his wrist. Springing to his feet, he ran. Luckily he found the entrance. He staggered out into the daylight screaming with terror. Hanging to his wrist with sharp teeth was the skull. He smashed it against a rock and examined his wrist. It was badly lacerated. Before he reached a settlement, his arm had become swollen with gangrene. He died several days later.

Another lonely hunter wandered far into the mountains and

lost his way. Determined to escape from a chaos of endless ravines, he climbed toward the peak of a high mountain. He was close to the summit when darkness forced him to halt. He wrapped himself in his blanket and lay down to rest.

In the night a terrible storm swept over the mountain. Lightning flashed and the crash of thunder made the earth tremble. A high wind hurtled over the barren, rocky ledges, whistling and howling like a legion of lost souls. Soon torrential rain fell.

The hunter crouched for shelter beneath an overhanging ledge. Abruptly the storm ended. In the light mist on the slope of the peak, the hunter saw a vision of a church. Within the church was a brightly lighted altar. Around the altar appeared a score of kneeling Indians. A white hand swept over their bowed heads, making the sign of the cross. The mist swirled and thickened. The church vanished. From the mist came wild, sweet music, rising and falling until the cadence merged with the moan of the wind.

The attack on St. Francis by Major Rogers's Rangers and their subsequent retreat through a cold, hostile wilderness were an event of great magnitude to the English colonists living on the frontier. In one savage battle the New England Rangers had wreaked a terrible vengeance on their enemies. The power of the Indian raiders of St. Francis was broken forever.

It was natural that as time went by, a number of myths and legends grew up about the expedition. Several of them concerned the loot which was taken from the Indian town by Rogers's men. A few pertained to the desertion of Amos Parsons.

In this story the historical accounts of the affair have been woven together with a few of the legends.

The Phantom Bridge

In early colonial times the settlers of Great Barrington, Massachusetts, constructed a long bridge across the Housatonic River. It resisted the spring floods for many years, providing a convenient crossing for a highway to the Hudson Valley. There is an old tale concerning this wooden bridge, a tale still told and retold in the upper Housatonic country, a story which taxes the credulity of the listeners.

A young gentleman, Gilbert Van Rensselaer, of Albany, New York, once fell in love with a charming young lady who lived in the township of Great Barrington. Her name was Anne Hopkins.

Although the distance between Albany and Great Barrington was a day's journey, the young man frequently rode to that settlement to meet his girl friend. After spending an evening at the Hopkins's home, he customarily stopped at a tavern for the night. In the morning he would continue his journey, crossing the long bridge to the Albany highway and thence home.

He was a personable youth, and Mr. Root, the tavernkeeper, was always happy to spend a few minutes chatting with him whenever he arrived.

One sultry day in July, Van Rensselaer set out on the long

ride to Great Barrington. It was a hot day and a lonely journey. The road traversed the Hudson Valley and climbed a range of hills to enter the gloomy vales of the Taconic Mountains. He met no one. As the day advanced, ranks of thick, black clouds formed on the western horizon, blotting out the light of the sun. On sable wings they spread over the sky. The air became heavy. The sound of insects, birds and animals ceased. The rider had a fearful impression that the earth had stopped moving, waiting in terror for the onslaught of a mighty tempest.

At long last the horse and rider began to descend into the Housatonic Valley. Two miles more would bring him to the Great Bridge. Another mile further would bring him to the tavern. Van Rensselaer had not traveled more than half of that distance before the darkness of night enveloped the countryside.

Darkness of night? No! It was not merely dark. It was as if he were riding through a black fog which absorbed every glimmer of light. Even the horse beneath him was invisible.

He tried to assure himself that the darkness was of no importance. His horse was familiar with the road. Dropping the reins, he allowed his steed to pick his own way, meanwhile attempting to control his uneasiness by conjuring visions of a rosy-hued future as the husband of the incomparable Anne Hopkins.

Suddenly the heavens let loose a deluge of rain over the countryside. In an instant the youth was soaked to his skin. The sound of the pelting raindrops became a roar drowning out all other sounds. Van Rensselaer had a fantastic impression that his horse was a boat, bobbing over turbulent seas. Abruptly the rain ceased falling. The youth blinked his eyes in surprise. A short distance in front of him were the brightly lit windows of the tavern.

Sometime later, dried out and comfortably seated in front

of the fireplace, Van Rensselaer sipped a hot rum drink while he chatted with the tavernkeeper.

"I must allow that I am surprised to see you," Mr. Root said. "How did you cross the river?"

"Oh, the usual way," the youth answered indifferently. "I rode across the Great Bridge."

"Impossible!" Root exclaimed. "The bridge is being repaired. Only today the carpenters tore off the flooring. There is not a single plank in place. Nothing but the pilings and stringers."

Van Rensselaer looked disturbed. "They must have put down a new flooring for that is where I crossed. I know of no other bridge over the river."

"This is strange, sir! Would you ride down to the bridge with me to investigate?"

Several minutes later, the two men, mounted and carrying lanterns, arrived at the banks of the river. In the darkness they could hear the noisy gurgling of rushing waters. Dismounting and holding their lanterns high, they advanced to the edge of the road. In the light from their lanterns they saw the bridge, a great brown skeleton of piles and stringers that disappeared into the darkness. Between the stringers not a board or plank could be seen—only the rushing water.

The Machimoodus Noise

Indians named the mountain Machimoodus, signifying "the place of noises." They claimed that it was the abode of Hobbamoko, Chief of the Evil Spirits. The early white settlers more prosaicly named it Mount Tom. Like a huge sugar loaf, it dominates the low rolling hills in Connecticut midway between Saybrook and Middletown. Until fairly recent times this huge lump of rock and earth was often shaken by subterranean quakes. Terrifying rumblings and explosions within the bowels of the mountain were spoken of as the Moodus Noises.

The early inhabitants of the region decided that the noises were caused by encounters within the mountain between Haddam witches, who practiced black art, and East Haddam witches, who engaged in white magic. They told gullible visitors that in the center of Mount Tom was a great cave, lighted by the blue glow of a large carbuncle. Here the witches met each evening to screech and fight, venting their evil tempers on one another. On a sapphire throne, Machimoodus sat, waving a large pitchfork and endeavoring to keep the bickering among his subjects within bounds. Whenever the quarrels became too violent, he would strike his pitchfork into the ground. Instantly a mighty gust of wind would blast the witches from the cave; great boulders tumbled and fell, shaking the earth with their violence.

166

This incredible explanation for the noises was more or less accepted until the arrival in the Moodus area of a famous British scientist by the name of Dr. Steele. It soon became known that he intended to stay and seek the cause of the frequent subterranean rumblings within the mountain.

At first Steele spent several months excavating and exploring near the base of the mountain. Later he built a small house on the side of Mount Tom, covering the windows and stuffing the keyhole to repel prying eyes. Nosy natives, prowling around the vicinity, reported that they had heard the ring and clatter of metal being worked on an anvil. The sound came from Dr. Steele's house. The working of metal on an anvil brought to mind a blacksmith's forge. A forge induced one to remember the hot fire required to anneal metal. The hot fire suggested Hell—and Hell being the abode of Satan, by some weird and obscure reasoning, convinced the local Yankees that the Englishman was a disciple of the Fiend.

One night a hunter marooned on the mountainside by darkness was startled to see a ghostly white light shining from the mouth of a cave. Overcome by curiosity the hunter advanced toward the light. Suddenly he saw Dr. Steele climb a rocky path and walk into the cave. Instantly a blood-red beam shone forth, its intensity blinding the hunter for a short time. When he was again able to see, the beam of light had vanished.

The following day a search party was organized. They explored the mountainside but found no cave, nor any trace of the absent Dr. Steele. However, a notebook filled with voluminous notes was found on a rocky ledge and was identified as belonging to the English savant. Many of the notations in the book referred to the Moodus Noises.

The noises (according to Dr. Steele's notes) were caused by two pearls which he had found and destroyed. He had discovered other pearls growing and was sure that in future years they would produce similar noises.

The doctor was never found, but the Machimoodus Noises did not recur for many years, confirming the Englishman's theories.

On May 16, 1791, the Machimoodus Noises again shook Mount Tom in a series of violent explosions followed by two sharp quakes which broke chimneys and dishes. These quakes were felt as far away as Boston and New York, and they created panic in cities and towns.

The day after the great quakes, a native who lived near the base of Mount Tom claimed that he had seen an old man climbing down from the mountaintop. Accosting the aged one when he reached the road, the native asked him what he was doing in so perilous an area. The old man mumbled some vague words, showed his interrogator two large and beautiful pearls and walked away toward the village of Haddam.

Since that day the mountain has been quiescent.

The Legend of Peter Rugg

Tom Cutter of Menotomy (now Arlington), Massachusetts, was the last person to see Peter Rugg alive. There is no doubt that Tom saw and spoke to Rugg that evening, and that Peter was very much alive at the time. Ghosts or apparitions are not noted for striking people on the nose—and that evening, Peter Rugg, in one of his frequent fits of temper, struck Cutter on his proboscis hard enough to draw blood.

The story begins a few years before the Revolution. At that time Peter Rugg lived in a large, comfortable house on Middle Street, Boston. He was a horse and cattle dealer, had a diligent wife, a lovely young daughter, and was considered to be a good citizen by most of his neighbors. However, he possessed a fiendish temper that overruled his judgment whenever he became angry.

One day late in the fall, Rugg harnessed his horse, a large Roman-nosed bay, and hitched it up to a light carriage for a business trip to Concord. It was a fine day, so he took his little daughter along for company. When they were returning to Boston that afternoon, a violent thunderstorm overtook them. Peter stopped at Tom Cutter's place in Menotomy for a dram of hot spiced rum, and his host urged him to spend the night there. In fact, Mr. Cutter, who had already had a few drams of rum, became very insistent, so insistent that Peter's hot temper began to boil.

"Don't be a fool, Rugg," Tom Cutter said. "Night will soon be here, and this pelting rain could be the death of your daughter. Can you not see that the storm is increasing in violence?"

"Let the storm increase," roared the angry Rugg. "I will see home tonight in spite of storm or the Devil or may I never see home again."

Peter raised the whip to his horse but his host grabbed his arm. That was when Tom Cutter received a punch in the nose from his irascible friend. Holding his hand to his bleeding nose, Tom watched Peter Rugg, his daughter, carriage, horse and all disappear into the rainy night. They did not reach home.

A week went by before the authorities, goaded into action by Mrs. Rugg and her neighbors, instituted a sharp search, but not a trace of the missing cattle dealer or his daughter was found.

Time passed. The snows of winter came and then gave way to the warm breezes of spring. Then Peter Rugg was seen on Middle Street.

It was late one night in May when the householders of the street were awakened by the clatter and rattling of a conveyance, traveling rapidly over the uneven cobbles. Thomas Felt, the gunsmith, leaned out of his window to see who could be traveling at such an unseemly hour. Looking up the street, Felt saw a carriage rapidly approaching—and seated in the rig were Peter Rugg and his daughter. The lateness of the hour, the effect of a dampening rain and the sight of a phosphorescent glow which appeared to envelop the conveyance and its occupants gave the gunsmith such a turn that a chill shook his lean frame and his teeth began to chatter.

The next day Felt told his neighbors of the appearance of Peter Rugg, and his account quickly became the leading topic of conversation on the street. They were careful, however, to say nothing of the strange sight to Mrs. Rugg.

The good neighbors again initiated a search for the missing man and his daughter, and this time several people were found who claimed to have seen the pair but always under strange circumstances.

The toll collector at the Charlestown Bridge claimed that on several occasions, always in a rainstorm, he had seen Peter Rugg driving his carriage over the bridge at a furious clip, his daughter holding onto his arm while the bay horse seemed to enjoy the racing pace. Because they refused to stop, the toll collector had been unable to collect his fee. Once, as the rig rolled by at a terrific clip, the angry bridge tender threw his stool at the horse. To his horror and amazement, he saw the stool pass through the animal and bounce off the guard rail on the other side of the bridge.

A sea captain, who had arrived from Providence on a stage, claimed that a man resembling the description of Rugg stopped the coach and asked the direction to Boston. The man, his carriage and a little girl seated beside him were dripping wet, even though it was a pleasant day. After receiving directions, the man thanked the stagecoach driver and set off at a swift pace toward Boston. Shortly afterward, a fast-moving thunderstorm overtook the coach and everyone was soaked.

After these testimonials the search for the missing cattle dealer was abandoned. But the stories of the appearances of Peter Rugg in various localities of New England still continued.

At the turn of the century the publisher of a Boston newspaper became interested in the many stories of Peter Rugg and asked an itinerant tin peddler if he had ever seen the man.

"Aye! That I have!" the peddler answered sourly. "I was unfortunate enough to see the man and his carriage within a fortnight, in four different states, and each time I was shortly afterward visited by heavy thunderstorms. If I meet him once more, I shall be forced to take out marine insurance on my wares."

The newspaperman next interviewed Adonariah Adams, the veteran driver of the Portland Mail. He was a fat genial man who usually beamed upon the world with a friendly smile, but he looked disturbed when the question was put to him.

"Yes! I have seen Peter Rugg," he admitted reluctantly. "One day after we drove through Newburyport, I noticed thunderheads in the southern sky and whipped the horses into a trot. Ahead of us, heavy streaks of lightning flashed across the horizon, and I realized that we were in for a nasty tempest. We ascended Witch-Hang Hill at a fast clip, and as we reached the top, something compelled me to look back down the road. There I saw Peter Rugg's carriage tearing after us, gaining fast. My horses took fright and began to run at a desperate and dangerous pace, but Rugg's great beast steadily gained until he was racing neck and neck with my wheelhorses. Suddenly a bolt of lightning struck the Rugg conveyance. In the instantaneous flash I saw Peter and his daughter glowing with fire like a horseshoe as it is taken from the blacksmith's forge. At the same time, flames and sparks cascaded from the mouth and ears of the huge bay horse, and I was almost stifled by the odor of brimstone, yet the bolt seemed to have no effect on the creature for the carriage continued its headlong pace. My horses were so frightened that they leaped from the road, wrecking the coach against a boulder." The driver of the Portland Mail shook his head slowly.

"It is my opinion," he vouchsafed, "that what I saw was the Devil's shade of Peter Rugg."

The last story concerning the appearance of Peter Rugg came from Rhode Island several years later.

An itinerant preacher, the Reverend Samuel Nickles, after a fortnight spent in the village of Wickford, packed his meager belongings, with the exception of his Bible, in the saddlebag, mounted his aged, nearsighted horse and departed for Providence. His worthy steed was blessed with the name of Romeo, a misnomer if there ever was one.

According to the story, this aged Pegasus and his master were overtaken by a fierce thunderstorm as they neared Quonset. There were no shelters so the pastor hunched his shoulders under his dripping coat, bowed his head and let his horse set the pace. The road skirted a large sloping rock and narrowed as it passed between two sandy hillocks. As Romeo plodded into the narrows, the Reverend Mr. Nickles heard the sound of a fast-approaching carriage. When the startled man looked up, he saw a rig racing toward him at a terrific speed. On the seat a pale, frightened man pulled on the reins while a girl held to his arm with both hands. The horse drawing the carriage was a huge, Roman-nosed bay whose eyes, in the misty half-light, shone like live coals.

In the narrows there was not enough room to avoid a collision. The frantic Romeo lunged up on his hind legs, flinging his rider through the air. The Reverend Mr. Nickles described a complete somersault and landed astride the huge bay.

"Stop! Stop!" he shouted in terror.

Instantly, a great bolt of lightning struck the ground nearby. The bay let out a neighing that was not of this world and dashed up the sloping side of the rock outcropping, tossing the Reverend Mr. Nickles unconscious to the ground.

When the unfortunate man regained consciousness, he was lying at the base of the rock. Romeo was nibbling grass nearby. The storm was over and the sun was again shining brightly. Staggering to his feet, he saw a set of cloven hoof tracks burned into the hard surface of the rock. Hastily mounting Romeo, the pastor left the vicinity as fast as his steed would travel.

Later the Reverend Mr. Nickles told of his encounter to several congregations in New England, and many curious folks traveled to Quonset to see the cloven hoof tracks in the rock. To this day the phenomenon beside Route 1 near the entrance to the Quonset Air Base is known as Devil's Foot Rock.

Although the stories of Peter Rugg were told and retold for many years after the Quonset affair, it is a strange fact that never again was he or his carriage reported to have been seen in New England.

The story of persons who are subject to rainy and foul weather, wherever they go, is an old one. There are German, Welsh and English renditions. The story of Peter Rugg is our New England version. It is a folktale of many variations.

Micah Rood's Apple Tree

Young Thomas Ayers shivered in the cold, damp air as he hurried along the Old County Road in Franklin, Connecticut. Ahead, the boy saw the huge trunk and spreading branches of the Old County Oak, a well-known landmark. Beyond, surrounded by stone walls, was a cluster of weathered buildings—the house, barn and pigpens of Micah Rood's farm. Close to the road a large apple tree raised gnarled branches toward the sky.

It had snowed hard the previous evening. Later the snow had turned to rain, melting much of the accumulation. Around the bases of trees and stone walls, snow patches lay white in the early morning light.

Suddenly Tom Ayers stopped in his tracks and stared in terror. Beneath the apple tree lay the battered body of a man. Spots and blobs of blood had stained the white snow. Taking to his heels, the boy ran to the nearby farmhouse of Joseph Picket. Arousing the farmer, young Ayers told of his discovery.

Within an hour town officials and a group of local farmers had gathered at the scene. The body was quickly recognized as that of an old Jewish peddler who often traveled through Franklin. He had been murdered by repeated blows from a hammer.

The pigkeeper, Micah Rood, on whose property the body had been found, was questioned by the officials. In a straightforward manner he told his interrogators that he had known Old Solomon the peddler for many years. Whenever Solomon was in the neighborhood, he visited the Rood farm and slept in the barn. Micah claimed that he had seen and talked to the old peddler the previous evening. According to his story, the old Jew had appeared nervous and apprehensive. He told Rood that two robbers had attacked him one night in a small tavern. Only his loud cries had frightened them away. He had been certain that the robbers were following him.

The investigators questioned all persons living within a seven-mile radius of the murder scene, but they learned nothing that could be used to indicate the identity of the killer. It seemed, however, that all of the local farmers were distrustful of Micah Rood. The officials found Solomon's heavy pack in the pigkeeper's barn. There was no evidence that it had been tampered with. Inside was a conglomeration of pots and pans, needles, pins, cheap jewelry, twine and other sundries. A leather purse containing three silver shillings and twenty copper pennies was found on the body.

The authorities impounded the money and the contents of the pack to pay the expenses of the investigation, and Old Solomon was buried in Potter's Field with scant ceremony. Afterward the investigation was dropped.

That winter many rumors concerning the murder were circulated in Franklin. It was said that the murdered peddler had always carried a large collection of diamonds, emeralds and rubies in a small sack which hung from a stout cord about his neck and was concealed beneath his shirt. The sack had not been found in or around the peddler's body by the investigators.

Another rumor was to the effect that a bloody hammer had been found in Micah's barn. When questioned about the implement, the farmer explained that he often used it to slaughter pigs. Strangely this explanation was accepted without further investigation.

Spring finally arrived. The dainty buds on apple trees unfolded, clothing dark branches with vestments of pink beauty and filling the air with fragrance.

A shocked whisper spread about Franklin like wildfire. Townspeople walked along Old County Road, stopping in groups to gaze in superstitious wonder at Micah Rood's apple tree. Under this tree a murder had been committed. Under this tree the battered body of Old Solomon had been found. Now, on every blossom on the tree a bright red spot, like a drop of blood, was distinctly seen. The observers gazed at the telltale blossoms and then stared reflectively at the Micah Rood farmhouse. Was the apple tree pointing an accusation at its owner?

The following summer Micah Rood was seldom seen by the townspeople. He avoided them whenever possible. He became moody and irascible, throwing stones at dogs and verbally abusing children who loitered near his property. In the fall Micah's apple tree held a bumper crop of large, shiny apples.

One morning Joseph Picket, walking to town on the Old County Road, observed Micah Rood standing beneath his apple tree, gazing at the laden branches. He reached up and picked an apple. Mr. Picket saw him take a pocket knife from his coat and cut into the fruit. For a long moment the pig farmer stared at the cut apple. Suddenly he threw the pieces away, gave a queer high cry and ran toward his house.

Picket shook his head in wonder. What had caused Rood to act so frightened? Micah had vanished into his house. After a pause of indecision, Picket climbed over the stone wall and picked an apple from the tree. With his knife he halved it. The flesh of the apple was a waxy white except in the center. Next to the core was an irregular red splotch, like a drop of blood.

Disturbed by his discovery, Joseph Picket hurried to Franklin. He showed the cut apple to several of his friends. Surprise turned to speculation, speculation to suspicion. A delegation of citizens aroused the town authorities and demanded that Micah Rood be arrested for the murder of Old Solomon the peddler.

The same afternoon the local officials went to the Rood farmhouse. They knocked on the door but there was no response. Forcing the door, they entered. Sitting in a straight-backed chair, facing the door, Micah Rood stared with glassy eyes at his unwelcome visitors. He was dead.

The farmhouse, barn and outbuildings were searched, but nothing of an incriminating nature was ever found. Rood was buried in a family plot on his farm. Spectators claimed that when his body was being lowered into the ground, the setting sun cast weird red beams over the farm.

Strangely the next year Micah Rood's tree produced only a handful of dwarfed, wizened apples, flecked with golden spots. Farmers living on the Old County Road claimed that they could see a likeness in the misshapen apples to the head of Old Solomon the peddler.

This plot appears to have been a favorite in colonial times. Versions of this story can be found in many New England town histories.

For Love of a Woman

For love of a woman men have committed some of the bravest, kindest and most chivalrous acts ever recorded in the annals of the human race. They have also, and for the same reason, performed cowardly, vile and inhuman deeds. Some of these episodes are dramatic.

The central character of this drama was a young lady by the name of Catherine Storm. From Passamaquoddy Bay to the shores of York Beach, she was considered the most beautiful woman living on the coast of Maine.

She was tall and slim, withal a delightfully curvaceous female, remindful of the ancient statues of Greek goddesses. Her chestnut hair framed an oval face, beautified by ruby red lips and intensely blue eyes. When she smiled, deep dimples added a fillip to her bewitching feminity. She lived with her father, Joel Storm, a retired sea captain, in a large white house on Ledge Hill, overlooking the sparkling salt water reaches of Pond Cove near Portland.

As a jar of honey attracts flies, so Catherine's charm drew the young men of the coast to her door. A good-natured but keen rivalry existed among them. Firmly believing in the old adage that "All is fair in love or war," they tried every conceivable trick to gain favor with their adored one. A bit of a co-

179

quette (as all women are), she enjoyed the game immensely.

Now two of the rivals for Catherine's hand were local youths, both fishermen who from childhood had been the closest of friends. Tom Wright and Jack Welch were their names, and their friendship for each other had often been likened to the classic camaraderie of Damon and Pythias. Even their rivalry for the affections of Catherine Storm apparently made little difference. They still were seen together, fishing, hunting or at drills, dances and house raisings.

Discouragement thinned the ranks of Catherine's suitors. Soon it became obvious that Tom Wright and Jack Welch were the favored ones. Nearly every evening, one of them would ascend Ledge Hill to the big white house on the summit, there to pay court to the captain's daughter. Suddenly fate seemingly made a choice.

Late one evening Jack Welch, repairing his skiff on a sandy strand near Pond Cove, was seen by a neighbor. That same night he disappeared. His family initiated a search for him. Fellow fishermen and friends combed the Pond Cove area but could find no trace of the missing man. His boat and tools were still on the beach where he had last been seen. If any evidence of foul play had been left on the sandy shores, it would have been obliterated by the tide.

Tom Wright was badly shaken by the disappearance of his friend. He took a major part in the search, often giving vocal indications of his grief. As the days went by, he became wan and extremely nervous. However, time has a way of healing sorrow. Within a fortnight he began walking up the steep road to Ledge Hill and the Storm house. A few months later he married Catherine Storm.

Time went by. Jack Welch was all but forgotten. Then, on the anniversary of his disappearance, a supernatural manifestation took place which frightened all who saw it. At dusk a huge ball of fire was seen to rise from the water about a mile from shore. With frightening speed, it hurtled through the air across the cove. Observers saw it strike Captain Storm's house and vanish. Later examination showed no evidence of the house's having been damaged in any way. From that day on, the fireball was seen at dusk on the anniversary of Jack Welch's disppearance.

Several years went by. Tom Wright with some of his friends, returning from a fishing trip, was delayed in reaching port by adverse winds. As they neared the entrance to Pond Cove, one of the party noted that it was the anniversary of Jack Welch's disappearance. Many nervous glances were cast seaward as the ship entered the cove. Suddenly the bright fireball was seen to arise from the sea and start its journey toward the white house on the hill. This time, the fireball paused briefly over the fishing boat before continuing to the Storm house, where it disappeared. The fishermen were startled by the vivid phenomenon. They were even more surprised by the abject terror displayed by one of the crew. Tom Wright had cowered in the waist of the ship, alternately shrieking and praying as the fireball hovered overhead. When the fishing boat docked, he hurriedly left the ship. He was never seen again in Pond Cove. A search was made but not a trace of him was found.

For two years Catherine waited in vain for some word concerning the fate of her husband. Eventually she remarried. Years went by. Children were born to Catherine, and she lived a happy, active and useful life.

One day a sailor from Portland arrived in Pond Cove. From a local fisherman he learned that the widow of Tom Wright had remarried and lived in the Storm house on Ledge Hill. He climbed the hill, nodding approvingly at the neat, well-kept house. He rapped on the door.

Catherine was in the kitchen making bread when she heard the knock. Wiping her hands on a towel, she went to the door.

A stranger, tanned and wrinkled by the sea, stood in the doorway. He touched his hat respectfully, handed her a letter and left without speaking a word.

The envelope was worn and stained. Catherine opened it. On a piece of cheap yellow paper, written in a weak, trembling hand, was a confession:

"I, Thomas Wright, about to depart this unhappy life, wish to make known to all concerned, that I murdered my best friend Jack Welch in a moment of passion. When Catherine Storm told me that she intended to marry Jack, I began to hate him for depriving me of the woman I loved. One evening, I saw him repairing his boat. Quietly, I crept up behind him. Picking up an adze, I struck him a terrific blow on the head. He died instantly. I carried his body to my boat and rowed until I was a mile from shore. There I threw the mortal remains of Jack Welch overboard. Later, I married Catherine and should have been happy but I could not forget my evil deed. In the night, I would awaken to find Jack's spirit sitting on the edge of my bed. In the whine of the wind, I heard his voice. The terrible fireball which arose from the sea where I threw his body was a flaming finger, pointing to my foul action. Every day I was afraid that Catherine would discover my secret. I left Pond Cove one night and walked to Portland. There I signed on a brig bound for France. From that day, I have wandered over the face of the earth, pursued by the accusing spirit of Jack Welch. Now I am about to die. God forgive me for my horrible deed."

The letter was signed: Thomas Wright.

The Haunted House of Watertown

It was a three-storied, rambling structure, half-hidden by a grove of somber hemlock. A carriage drive circled in front of the house, then slipped unobtrusively through a weathered, wooden gateway, thence to the main road between Cambridge and Waltham, Massachusetts. Now it is gone, torn down in the path of civic progress, thus perhaps laying to rest for all times the ghostly characters which once tenanted it. Old-time residents of the vicinity claimed that there were evil emanations from the mansion which apparently affected the people of the neighborhood. They pointed to the abnormally high incidence of crimes of violence which had occurred in an area of a mile circumscribing the haunted house. Most of them also had tales to tell of specters which had been seen roaming the grounds near the house. Few of the local citizens were brave enough to linger near the place after dark, yet scores of them claimed to have seen apparitions or heard the bloodcurdling screams of a woman in mortal terror. Ghost hunters, attracted by the reputation of the mansion, spent many hours searching the house and grounds. The stories of their adventures in the realm of the supernatural, coupled with the known history of the house, make a fascinating if somewhat somber tale.

The original owner of the place was a cultivated gentleman

from a distinguished New England family. In his youth he had been a wild blade, but after his graduation from Harvard, he seemed to have settled down. He built the mansion in Watertown and a few months later married the daughter of a well-known magistrate.

Apparently he spent a rather aimless life without recourse to work in either business or the professions, yet he always seemed to possess unlimited funds.

In the course of time, three children were born to the family, and for several years the household seemed to be a model of happiness and contentment. Quite suddenly the domestic harmony was broken.

A young woman named Alice Morrow came to live in the mansion as governess of the children. She was an orphan from Philadelphia, without a friend in New England. Old Molly, the housekeeper who lived with the family for many years, said that she was an extremely beautiful woman. Slim and shapely, she had dark brown eyes and a wealth of wavy chestnut hair. Her voice was soft and musical.

Within a few months after the arrival of Alice Morrow, a change occurred in the relations of the household. Molly noticed increasing friction between husband and wife. Quarrels and recriminations in loud and angry tones were heard by the servants, and an increasing intimacy between the master and Alice the governess was observed. When warm weather arrived, the man began to go on long rides with Alice, leaving his wife desolate at home. The rides of the pair became a daily custom. Often they did not return until after midnight. Alice, with a key given to her by the wayward husband, would unlock the door and enter the house. With a light step and furtive glance, she would hurry up the front stairway to her chamber. On most occasions she wore a black silk dress, a heavily fringed mantle and a black lace bonnet. Mornings and early afternoons she devoted to her young charges. Unconscious of the sordid drama unfolding in their home, the children showered her with affection.

As time went by, the wife, stricken with grief over the infidelity of her husband and the dreadful discipline needed to meet and converse with the woman who had supplanted her in his affections, began to waste away. Finally in desperation, she left her home and went to live with her mother, taking the children with her.

It would be supposed that the lovers, without the restraint imposed by the presence of the wife and children, would revel in their freedom. Strangely this was not the case. Perhaps conscience and remorse began to fester. Perhaps the pair became surfeited with sin. Whatever the reason, the master became moody and abstract. He began to drink heavily. Alice, her eyes filled with woe, spent much of her time in her room. From behind the closed door, Old Molly often heard the girl weeping bitterly.

Unexpectedly the man's financial affairs became a matter of concern. Creditors began to dun him until he was frantic. Surprisingly his mother-in-law came to his aid. She loaned him a large sum of money without interest. A few weeks after this financial transaction, Alice Morrow disappeared. The master let it be known that she had returned to Philadelphia.

The wife and children returned to the mansion, and again peace and harmony prevailed in the household. Then fate or the Devil decreed that another woman would cross the threshold.

Her name was Claire and she was the master's niece. Forced by the death of a sister to find means of livelihood, she asked her uncle to hire her as governess of his children. She was very young and beautiful, too tempting a morsel to escape the amorous pursuit of her uncle. Within a short time he had seduced her, and she, poor girl, fell hopelessly in love with him. The conduct of the lovers was scandalous. Again the wife left her home to accept the bounty of her mother. However, this time the affair was noised about the town, and the master of the mansion was ignored or treated with contempt by his neighbors.

Again financial distress began to dog the culprit. He was forced to mortgage the estate to pay his pressing debts. Soon this money was gone, and he was obliged to sell his horses and carriage. Suddenly he came into possession of a considerable sum of money. He paid his debts and began to spend lavishly. Strangely no one connected his sudden affluence with the disappearance of an itinerant peddler named Carrol who was reported to carry large sums of money with him.

One day Old Molly heard the angry voices of the master and his niece Claire in the library. They were engaged in a bitter argument. The old housekeeper went to market. When she returned, the girl was gone. The man told Molly that his niece had left the house to visit friends. Claire was never seen again.

Alone in the big house with only the old housekeeper for company, the master again began to drink heavily. Four years later he died. The mansion was sold to pay his creditors.

A tradesman from Boston with a large and growing family bought the property. His family stayed only a few months in the mansion. Unable to endure the strange sounds which echoed day and night through the house, they sold it and moved to another town.

Several other families in turn occupied the place but could not stand the ghostly manifestations. The house gained a reputation as being haunted, and for several years it remained vacant.

Then a financier who had acquired a nearby farm property bought the mansion to house his farm manager. This farmer, Thomas King, a robust man in the prime of life, was courageous to a marked degree. For four years, with his wife, son and daughter, he lived in the house, apparently unafraid of the ghostly apparitions and nocturnal manifestations which had gained it such a sinister reputation. During this period, however, he had sublet several of the rooms, only to have his tenants leave the premises in a hurry. Later the rooms were rented to ghost hunters, who spent many hours trying to find an explanation for the seemingly supernatural occurrences. Mr. King's description of his own experiences while living in a haunted house are interesting.

The first night in the mansion the Kings had as guests a lady and her sick husband who occupied the front chamber over the parlor. The Kings bedroom was on the opposite side of the hall. They slept soundly that night, hearing no unusual noises. In the morning their guests inquired if they had heard someone moving about in the upper rooms during the night. When the Kings admitted that they had slumbered without disturbance, the lady guest disclosed that she had been awakened by loud knocks in her room. Frightened by the sounds, she had huddled in her bed. Suddenly the house rocked from foundation to attic as if in the throes of an earthquake, and several doors opened and closed with great violence.

The following night, a few minutes before midnight, Thomas King was awakened by a pounding on the door of the woodshed, a lean-to attached to the kitchen. It sounded like the blows of an axe. King's first thoughts were that burglars were breaking into the house. Slipping on his trousers and lighting a candle, he crept downstairs to the kitchen. Blow after blow resounded, followed by a loud crash as if the outside door had fallen into the woodshed. Rushing to the kitchen door, King placed his foot against it and awaited the attack by the burglars. His only weapon was a flatiron. At first he heard two voices and then quick, sharp blows of an axe. In a few minutes the sound ceased. All was silent in the house. The brave farmer, holding the flatiron ready, unbolted the kitchen door and walked into the woodshed. It was unoccupied; the outside door was locked and everything was in its accustomed place.

Somewhat shaken, King returned to his bed. At midnight he was aroused by his wife, who said the bell on the front door had rung violently. Again he lit the candle, donned a robe and descended the stairs to the front door. The bell rang again. Tom King opened the door. In the clear moonlight he saw standing in the driveway a carriage drawn by a white horse. A gust of wind blew out the candle. He re-entered the house to relight it. When he looked outside again, the carriage was gone. The uncanniness of the affair sent shivers up and down his spine. Carefully he closed and locked the door. As he walked toward the stairs, he felt the soft pressure of a woman's hand on his arm. A pleasing perfume permeated the air, and an unseen form glided swiftly by with a rustling sound as of heavy silk. It rapidly ascended the stairs. King followed. He saw nothing, but distinctly heard the rustle of silk and light footsteps on the carpet. A door to an empty bedroom opened and closed. Silence again encompassed the house. He opened the bedroom door and peered within. The room was bare and deserted.

Returning to his room, he lay down on his bed and was soon asleep. His wife lay awake, uneasy, feeling an unearthly chill in the air. She was startled by a sharp rap on the bedroom door. Shaking her husand awake, she told him through chattering teeth of the disturbance. Again Tom King lit a candle and went to the door. The hallway was empty, but again he heard the rustle of silk.

In the morning the lady guest told the Kings that about midnight a strange man entered her room and walked to her bedside. He looked at her for a moment—then vanished. He was tall, distinguished-looking, with prominent features and slightly graying hair. This was a fair description of the first owner of the house.

Mrs. King was ironing one day in the kitchen. As she paused

in her work, she heard a sound like the whetting of a knife on a flint stone. The sound came from the pantry. She called her son, and together they opened the pantry door. Everything was in place. There was nothing disturbed.

Twice the Kings were disconcerted by piercing screams of a woman, apparently coming from the cellar. Both times Tom King descended to the dank, dark, cobwebby confines of the cellar to investigate. The only untoward thing he ever found there was a board stained with dark spots which might have been blood.

A lady from Rhode Island who claimed to possess the gift of spirit vision once visited the mansion with a male companion. Tom King gave them permission to hold a vigil through the night in the library. At midnight the pair heard a noise, as if earth was being shoveled in the cellar. As the man arose to investigate, the woman grasped his hand.

"Don't go!" she said. "It is the tall man. He is digging a grave for the woman whom he murdered."

The same night the pair heard footsteps in the hall and the sound of a woman weeping. When they opened the library door the sounds ceased. The gifted lady claimed that she saw a beautiful woman with a pallid face, a wealth of chestnut hair, wearing a black silk dress and a fringed silk mantle, walking slowly toward the stairs.

Another woman who was said to have the gift of spirit sight visited the house in the daytime with two female companions. When they reached the library, the seer claimed that a spirit had asked her if it might possess her body for a short time. The woman indicated a willingness to do so, providing the Kings were agreeable to the experiment. The Kings consented, and in a short time a group of twelve men and women congregated in the library.

The gifted lady knelt for prayer. Then, arising to her feet, in an entirely different voice and mannerism, she introduced herself as Claire, niece of the former owner of the mansion. She confessed that she had fallen in love with her uncle and had had illicit relations with him. After his wife left the house with the children, her uncle had dismissed all the servants with the exception of the housekeeper. They had been extremely happy at first. Then a change came over him. He became morose and uncommunicative. Despite her love she had often been repelled by a certain ruthlessness in her uncle's character. One day he murdered a peddler. The deed was done in the daytime. Complaining of an injured back, he had asked the peddler to saw some wood for him. While the peddler was thus engaged, her uncle crept up behind him and murdered him with an axe. Claire was in her room at the time and knew nothing of the crime. The next morning she had inadvertently entered the woodshed and was horrified to see blood on the ground and splattered on the outside door. In his haste to hide the body and rifle the peddler's pack, her uncle had neglected to remove the incriminating signs. She had run into the library where her uncle was drinking and accused him of the crime.

"Don't be a little fool," he said to her. "I needed his money. I have no liking for peddlers. I would kill a hundred if I could get rich by so doing."

Claire told him of the bloodstains which she had seen in the woodshed. That afternoon he removed the incriminating door, smashed it to pieces with an axe and replaced it with a new door. He then threw dirt over the bloodstains on the ground. That night, after a lover's embrace, he strangled her.

After telling this story in the first person, the seer collapsed. She remained in a stupor for two days. Finally she revived.

Several years went by. The financier sold his property, and the Kings moved to Connecticut. The haunted house, empty and neglected, was shunned by the people of Watertown.

Once a group of young men from Harvard, intrigued by the mansion's reputation, received permission to inspect the premises. With painstaking care, they examined every inch of the grounds and the house. In a vault, hidden by weeds, they found a luxuriant switch of woman's hair. It was wavy and golden brown. Evidently it had been removed with a piece of the scalp. Several flakes of flesh still clung to the roots.

After the searchers left the premises, it was rumored that they had discovered the skeletons of three adults, piled together like cordwood and hidden in a secret room in the cellar. The rumor was never verified.

So even the ending is a mystery. Eventually, the haunted mansion was torn down.

face. With painstaking care, they examined every inch of the ground and the house for a clue. But when they looked they found a luxuriant section of wallpaper torn. It was heavy, and golden brown, but a piece had been removed with a piece of the wall. Several tacks in the still hung to the paper.

After the searchers left the premises, it was reported that they had discovered the existence of their sliding pilot regaining her livelihood and hidden in a secret room in the cabin. The pump ? was never touched.

So even the ending is a mystery. Eventually, the haunted mansion is torn down.

TALES OF

MALEVOLENT MALEFACTORS, OF

COUNTERFEITERS AND PIRATES,

AND THE CAREER OF A FAMOUS

HIGHWAY ROBBER.

Rehoboth's Lady Counterfeiter

One of the earliest success stories of a New England home industry involved a most remarkable woman: Mary (Peck) Butterworth, of Rehoboth, Massachusetts. Her specialty was manufacturing money. Furthermore, this talented housewife was probably the most successful counterfeiter ever to operate in New England. And operate she did. From 1716 to 1723, in her busy kitchen workshop, she turned out hundreds of spurious notes, almost exact copies of "bills of credit" which were at that time issued by the governments of Massachusetts, Connecticut and Rhode Island.

Mary Peck was the daughter of a Rehoboth tavernkeeper who was related to most of the leading citizens of southern Massachusetts and Rhode Island, a circumstance which must have aided her in her business ventures. She was a robust, rather pretty young lady with a forceful character. It was said that she possessed a good deal of influence over her fellow citizens of the town. At the age of twenty-five, she married John Butterworth, an able young housewright and carpenter. (It is a commentary on Mary's character that her neighbors usually referred to John as "Mary Peck's husband.")

Young Butterworth's affairs were prosperous. He owned his own home and several tracts of land in nearby Attleborough, and had two carpenters, Arthur Noble and Hugh Beatties, working for him. He was doubtless a good family man, and his wife was probably in better financial circumstances than the average married woman of that period.

However, Mary was not satisfied. She loved money, but money was scarce. Most of the colonists of that day used the barter system for goods or services.

So Mary made the best of things. She ruled her house and husband, gave birth to two lively children, attended church regularly—and dreamed of money, large sums of gold and silver coins.

During King George's War, the colonial governments found themselves handicapped by the lack of some medium of exchange. Money was needed to pay the debts incurred by frequent military expeditions. To overcome this deficiency, each colony issued paper currency known as "bills of credit." They were crudely printed and easily counterfeited. Evidently many of our Yankee forebears held few qualms against counterfeiting and passing the illegal product. Within a short time a number of ingenious and artful New Englanders made or procured engraved plates, presses and paper, and went into the business of making bills of credit. Most of these enterprising businessmen, however, were soon detected and arrested. The possession of a printing press, engraved plates or counterfeit bills usually was enough evidence to convict them.

Mary Butterworth was cognizant of the many attempts to counterfeit bills of credit and also of the numerous unlucky moneymakers who were convicted for possessing fraudulent bills, engraving plates or presses. Despite this knowledge, she resolved to enter the field but to discover some method which would not require incriminating plates or a press. After experimenting for several months, she devised a method that not only was ingenious but left no evidence for the authorities to use against her. Her process was to lay a piece of starched muslin on a genuine bill of credit and run over it lightly with a hot iron. This left an impression of the bill on the muslin. She then placed the muslin over a blank piece of paper and pressed down hard with the flatiron, transferring the impression onto the paper. Then with a fine quill pen, she traced over the impression, taking care to duplicate the thickness of the lines. When the counterfeit bill was finished, the muslin was tossed into the fireplace, thus destroying the evidence.

When Mary was ready to begin her venture, she organized a tight little group of relatives to help her in her homework. The family venture employed three of her brothers, Nicholas, Israel and Stephen, and the wife of Nicholas, Hannah Peck. Mary, aided by Hannah, traced the fine impressions on the paper. Israel was an expert in forming quill pens, his skill enabling the tracers to duplicate the thickness of the letters and designs on the original bill of credit.

Mary Butterworth also organized a sales force to pass her product to unsuspecting merchants and innkeepers. She had seven passers, all residing at that time in Rehoboth. Two of them were her husband's hired men, Hugh Beatties and Arthur Noble. The others were Deputy Sheriff Daniel Smith, two brothers by the name of Chaffee and Nicholas Camp, and Camp's young sister Elizabeth. They bought the counterfeits from Mary at half price and disposed of them at taverns and mercantile houses in Newport, Providence, Boston, Salem and other towns.

Massachusetts and Rhode Island officials soon became aware that a large number of counterfeit bills were circulating throughout the colonies, but they were such exact copies of the genuine issues that they were accepted without question. The Rhode Island five-pound bill of the issue of July, 1715, one of Mary's favorites, was passed so extensively that the government of that colony was forced to cancel the issue and replace it with another.

Circumstances pointed to Rehoboth as the center of the counterfeiting ring. In September, 1722, the Court of Quarter Sessions at Bristol issued a warrant against Mr. Daniel Smith and others of the town of Rehoboth, directing the court officers to search houses for counterfeiting plates. Nothing was found, and the tight-mouthed Rehobothites refused to give any information to the searchers.

It began to look as if Mary Butterworth's illicit business would never be halted. However, in every ring there are weak segments. Arthur Noble proved to be the blunderer who tipped off the authorities.

Young Noble, on the eighteenth of July, 1723, borrowed a horse from his employer and rode to Newport to witness a gruesome spectacle, the public hanging of twenty-six pirates.

Arthur arrived early. He had a plentiful supply of Mary's counterfeit bills in his pocket, and the long ride had made him thirsty. In a Newport tavern he met three young ladies of Rehoboth who were also in Newport to observe the hanging. He invited them to join him. They were happy to oblige. Braggingly he displayed a handful of bills of credit and treated them with the liberality of a Croesus. The tavernkeeper's wife became suspicious. She summoned a warden and Noble was taken into custody. In a drunken humor he admitted that the bills in his possession were counterfeit. He implicated Nicholas Camp, who was in Newport at the time.

Camp was arrested and brought before a magistrate, where he broke down under questioning and confessed that he had passed several bogus bills of credit. Moreover, he told the interested official, in the minutest detail, the modus operandi of Mary Butterworth's moneymaking business.

On the fifteenth of August three deputy sheriffs arrived in Rehoboth and arrested John Butterworth, his wife Mary, Israel Peck, Nicholas Peck and his wife Hannah, Daniel Smith and

Hugh Beatties. They were taken to Bristol, charged with counterfeiting and uttering, and confined to the jail to await the next session of the court. On the tenth of September they were brought before Colonel Byfield for preliminary examination. The Colonel ordered John Butterworth and Nicholas Peck released from custody. Israel Peck and Mary Butterworth were returned to jail.

Meanwhile, in Newport, Arthur Noble and Nicholas Camp began to protest their innocence, claiming that their confessions were obtained under duress. The authorities could find no one who would admit that they had received spurious bills of credit from the pair. Reluctantly the rascals were released from jail and admonished to leave Rhode Island at once.

In Bristol County, the counterfeiting case came before the court on the fourteenth of September, 1723. The findings of the court were as follows:

"The bills of presentment exhibited against Israel Peck and Mary Butterworth for forging, counterfeiting and uttering bills of credit returned to the court by the Grand Jury for the body of the county of Bristol with ignoramus written thereupon. Daniel Smith, Mary Butterworth, Israel Peck, Hugh Beatties and Hannah Peck discharged by proclamation."

Thus the case ended. Because of the lack of evidence, all of the counterfeiters were discharged, but the publicity involved put an end to Mary's business.

She continued to live in Rehoboth, reared a family of seven children and attended church regularly. She died in 1775 in her eighty-ninth year. At her funeral, she was eulogized as "a worthy Christian lady who had ever lived a goodly and blameless life."

In this day and age, it is difficult to understand the viewpoint of citizens of Old New England in regard to counterfeiting. Evidently, except in the eyes of the law, it was not considered a very culpable act. Several instances have been recorded where groups of sympathetic citizens broke into jails and released counterfeiters awaiting trial or punishment.

Black Sam Bellamy

Black Sam Bellamy! He was a *real* pirate. Not a one-voyage buccaneer like Captain Kidd. Neither was he a persnickety brigand of the sea such as Captain Ben Hornigold who pursued a private vendetta against Spaniards, killing and robbing them without compunction, yet refusing to seize the wealth of French, Dutch and English shipping. Yes, sir! Black Sam was an honest-to-goodness villain at all times, ever ready for a fight or frolic. He would slit a throat just as quickly as he would double-cross a comrade. Gold was his deity.

Sam was an Englishman, a west countryman, a massive, powerful brute of a man. He was distinguished by a great shock of bushy black hair, a square-cut black beard, and piercing, dark brown eyes which sometimes appeared black as jet. Because of these characteristics, he was known as Black Sam Bellamy.

One legend claims that Bellamy with the aid of four rascally followers stole a small sloop and sailed her across the broad Atlantic and into Cape Cod Bay. The Bay at that time was a fisherman's paradise. Here brawny men worked long and hard, catching and salting codfish, a pursuit which was healthy but not very profitable.

Black Sam worked for a while as a fisherman, but the profits were too small. He was forever dreaming of the pot of gold buried at the end of the rainbow. Gold! Heaps of gold. These dreams were the loadstone of his existence. With his four rascals and an ex-pirate named Paul Williams from Newport, Rhode Island, he began to plan an expedition to the Spanish Main to search for the wrecks of Spanish treasure ships.

Meanwhile, Sam became infatuated with a Cape Cod girl, the lonely daughter of a farmer. Postponing the treasure voyage, he wooed her. He was a wild, tempestuous devil, the type which seems to appeal to many women. She fell in love with him, and he treated her as if she was a wench of the taverns.

This interlude did not tarnish Bellamy's bright dreams of gold. One day he kissed his little sweetheart good-by, promising to return and marry her. Away sailed the little sloop, leaving behind a grief-stricken lassy. With the empty dreams of golden adventure driving him on, Black Sam quickly forgot his Cape Cod mistress.

She, poor girl, waited in hope which, as the months passed by, turned to despair. She was to have a baby, Bellamy's child. She could not hide her condition. Her neighbors, descendants of the Pilgrim Fathers, labeled her a sinner, cutting her cruelly with their scorn. Even her father turned his face from her. In misery and agony of spirits she left her home. In a ramshackle fish shed, hidden among the dunes, her child was born and died—all in the compass of a gray and stormy day. The skies wept; the east wind sang a dirge among the scrub pines, but no human was near to offer her solace.

Afterward she refused to live near her condemners. She dug a small grave in a pine grove near the fish shanty. Here she buried her child, marking the grave with a rude cross. She continued to live alone amid the dunes, eking out a scanty living by God knows what means. Every day she climbed to the top of the sand hills and gazed out to sea, praying for the return of her lover.

Meanwhile, Black Sam Bellamy arrived in the Caribbean.

For weeks he sailed among jewel-like islands searching for the wreckage of Spanish treasure ships. Sir William Phips had once done the same, with spectacular results. He had found a treasure valued at more than a million pounds. With his share of the gold, he had purchased a title and a governorship. Surely Bellamy could do as well.

The rascals and their black-haired leader searched diligently, but nary a wreck could they find. The weather was hot. The sloop's bottom became fouled with seaweeds and barnacles. The ship's stores of pork and beef spoiled. Weevils made their home in the hardtack. Bellamy and his crew grumbled and ate fish. Williams remarked that "it would be more seemly to die as a pirate with a full stomach than to starve hunting for wrecks."

There came the day when they careened the sloop to scrape the seaweeds and barnacles from the bottom. They selected a small island with a sandy shore. It was a ticklish job to lay a ship on its side without injuring masts, stays or ribs. This time ill luck attended their effort. Several timbers used to support and distribute the weight of the sloop slipped, and the vessel fell heavily on its side. Several strakes were broken and the hull was sprung. The little ship would never sail again.

Black Bellamy and his rascals, thus marooned on a desert island, ate sea turtles and birds—and waited.

Their enforced patience was finally rewarded. One day, two ships bore down on the island, two pirate ships aprowling. One was the *Mary Anne*, under the command of Captain Ben Hornigold. The other was the *Postillion*, commanded by the bloodthirsty brigand Louie Lebous.

Bellamy and his men were taken aboard the *Mary Anne*. "What will it be?" Captain Ben asked the marooned treasure hunters. "Sail with us, share and share alike or—stay on the island and rot."

"Cut their throats," Louie Lebous suggested pleasantly.

"Faith! Happy we'd be to join your band," Bellamy said. "Ye have men, guns and proper vessels. 'Tis a prosperous trade."

"Good! It's agreed! Share and share alike!" said Captain Ben. "There is room for you here aboard the *Mary Anne.*"

Later in the day the two pirate ships spread their sails and scudded over the silver-tipped waves toward the Spanish islands where rich booty might be won by brave lads. Bellamy and Williams stood by the rail, idly watching a school of porpoises. The sun was high and most of the freebooters were napping in shaded portions of the deck.

"Glad I would be to sail this ship myself. With you in command of the *Postillion,* we could win a fine fortune. Staunch, large ships these are—fast sailers for a trade needing swift vessels to chase the fat, rich merchantmen. We must win friends among the crew. Perhaps we may someday become their leader."

"Not the *Postillion!* Lebous is a hard man," Williams commented.

"Aye! He knows not the way of proper seafarers. Methinks he'd cut a blind man's throat to steal the pennies o' his begging."

Seaboots sounded on the deck behind the pair.

"This sun has been known to addle the brains of ambitious men, Mr. Bellamy," said Hornigold. "It would be better to mingle with the other members of the brotherhood."

Unexpectedly the *Mary Anne* and the *Postillion* captured a large Indiaman bound for Holland with a rich cargo of logwood. It was an English ship with an English crew. For two days the pirates sailed alongside their prize while Hornigold and Lebous angrily argued over the disposition of her. Later it became known to the pirate crews that Captain Ben would not allow an English ship to be plundered. The officers of the Indiaman were freed and returned to their ship. Sardonically they saluted the pirates with a ten-gun salute and sailed away toward Jamaica. There were many disgruntled sailors aboard the *Mary Anne* and the *Postillion* who cursed heartily to see a fortune slip from their grasp because of Hornigold's foolish principles.

Black Sam Bellamy fostered the discontent. He said aloud that if the brotherhood ever elected *him* as their commander, "damned if he would at any time let mollycoddling sentiment stand in the way of securing riches for his crew." A bright gold English sovereign bought the pleasures of liquor and women just as quickly as a Spanish ducat.

From that day on, the crew of the *Mary Anne* began to speak openly of an election. Lebous backed Bellamy. Finally, late in May, Sam challenged Captain Ben's leadership. On the Isle of Pines, the pirate crew held their election for captain. Sam won by a ninety to twenty-six margin.

In a small snow (a square-rigged, briglike ship), Hornigold sailed away with the few crewmen who were willing to follow him.

Luck smiled on Bellamy. Ship after ship surrendered to the flaming guns of the two pirate vessels. Captured sailors were given the choice of joining the brotherhood or walking the plank. Most of them joined.

Near the Isle of Saba the *Mary Anne* and her consort captured the *Sultana*, a fast new ship laden with fine liquors, salted beef and milled wheat. Bellamy double-crossed his partner by placing the *Mary Anne* in charge of his friend Paul Williams and taking over the command of the prize. Louis Lebous, finding his ship outgunned by the combined armament of the *Mary Anne* and the *Sultana*, sullenly withdrew and sailed away.

On January 9, 1717, Black Sam and Paul Williams, sailing their ships through the Windward Passage, sighted the eighteen-gun galley *Whydah* and gave chase. The pirates overtook their prey and fired a broadside across her deck. Quickly the captain of the *Whydah* surrendered.

It was a rich prize. Below, in the captain's cabin, was a specie chest containing gold and silver coins to the amount of twenty thousand pounds. Bellamy and Williams stared at the treasure, their eyes alight with greed. Brimming full, the chest held ducats, doubloons, guilders, pieces of eight, louis d'ors and English guineas.

"We need not tell the crew of finding this chest," Williams whispered. "Only the captain knows."

"Aye! We must remedy that," Black Sam said grimly. With the speed of a serpent, he drew his sword and killed the captain of the *Whydah*.

"Now we shall keep it for ourselves—share and share alike," he said. Carefully he locked the chest and hid it under the captain's bunk. Then laughing merrily he turned to Williams. "Would you not agree that we have made great advancement in this world of fools?"

Under Bellamy's directions, the supplies and guns aboard the *Sultana* were transported to the *Whydah*. Later the *Sultana* was sold to a Dutch trading company.

One day the pirates held a council meeting in the captain's cabin of the *Whydah*. Here they formulated plans to attack the rich city of Newport in Rhode Island. Afterward they all agreed that Bellamy was a bold fellow.

"Sail into Newport with cannons blazing," he had said. "The only defense of the seaport is an earthen fort mounting a few six-pounders. The *Whydah*'s guns will blow it apart. The Quakers who rule the town are men of peace. They have no militia to oppose a landing. The brotherhood will sack the rich merchant's mansions, taking their pick of the handsome Quaker women. We can attack, sack and sail out of the harbor before any organized resistance can be assembled."

The pirates gave a mighty roar of approval. It was a wonderful plan.

So Bellamy's fleet sailed northward. Off the coast of Virginia they captured the brig *Tanner* of London. Several members of her crew signed on as pirates. Among them was John Shuan, a man of education, a troubadour and poet.

Shortly after, they were overtaken by a great storm, a howling hurricane, blowing west by north. It scattered the pirate fleet. The *Mary Anne* lost her mainsail. On the *Whydah* both the main and mizzen masts were sprung, and the ship began to take water. The frightened pirates manned the pumps and worked madly to keep the ship afloat. It was touch and go for a while.

After the storm the battered fleet assembled off Block Island. Bellamy decided to postpone the attack on Newport. His ships were in a sad state. They would have to be beached for badly needed repairs.

Skirting the Cape Cod coast, the buccaneers captured a small sloop laden with fresh hides. Captain Beers of Boston, commander of the prize, was unimpressed by the strength of the pirate fleet.

"Best be gone," he advised Bellamy grimly. "The Massachusetts cruiser is searching these seas for you. They will blow your whole fleet apart—blast you betwixt wind and water."

The Beers ship was scuttled. Her master and crew were crowded into a leaky longboat and allowed to depart.

Sailing northward, Black Sam searched the Maine coast for a safe haven to careen and repair his ships. The fleet hesitated at the mouth of the Penobscot River, then decided to sail further north. In the wilderness encompassing the Machias River, they found their haven. Two and a half miles above the river's mouth they anchored their ships. Guns and everything of weight were transported ashore. Under Paul Williams's supervision, a strong fort was constructed of tree trunks reinforced by boulders and earth. The cannon were mounted on gun platforms placed in such a manner that their fire could cover the river. On the sloping shore above the fort the pirates built two dozen thatched huts.

"What shall we name our fair town?" asked Bellamy with a touch of pride.

"Call it Norumbega, the City of Gold," suggested John Shuan the poet. "Old legends say that it exists on the banks of a great river in this Maine country. It is said to contain fabulous buildings, vast treasures and many beautiful women. An Englishman claimed that he visited the place. Perhaps he lied. He also said that he had walked from Florida, the Land of the Fountain of Youth. On this coast, he met French traders who treated him kindly."

"It must have been a lie," Williams commented.

"What know ye of this country?" Bellamy asked the poet.

"I know much—or little. Much from hearsay, little otherwise. This vast tract of land betwixt the Kennebec River and the Saint Johns River to the north is claimed by both the French and English, yet neither has force enough to hold it. May I be so bold, sir, as to propose that we claim this land by rights of occupancy. Here we can build a great pirate empire. What say you? Would ye care to be an emperor?"

Black Sam grinned but said naught.

The impish John Shuan bowed low. "Why not? Rome, mistress of the ancient world, was founded by a couple of sheep stealers and populated by runaway slaves. Ye have over two hundred men who are not strangers to the art of war. Raise every man to some small rank in the state. Take the Indians under your protection and offer free land to the distressed and malcontents of the French and English colonies. Build ships and make war on all nations. Have they not already declared war on us? After we win a few victories on the seas, they will send ambassadors here to negotiate with you and to court your alliance."

"What would you be in this new kingdom," asked Bellamy.

The poet made a courtly bow. "Pray appoint me as your prime minister."

After the ships were repaired, Bellamy set out to obtain recruits from among the fishermen at Newfoundland. He left a strong garrison to man the fort. The buccaneers captured some small prizes but found few sailors desperate enough to join the pirate brotherhood.

While sailing alone in the vicinity of the Island of Saint Paul, the *Whydah* lookouts sighted a large sail, and Bellamy gave orders to close in. It was a near fatal mistake. The stranger was a French frigate of thirty-six guns, transporting French soldiers to Quebec.

The French commander at first decoyed the pirates by simulating an appearance of desperate flight. However, when the *Whydah* closed in and began to fire a bow gun, the Frenchman, in a brilliant maneuver, jibbed his speeding ship. Heading now directly toward the pirate ship, he dropped his gunports, revealing his formidable batteries. Before Bellamy's gunners could sight their cannon, the French frigate sent a broadside crashing into the *Whydah*. Chain shot and grape chewed the sails and rigging, killing several of the pirates. Cheered by this success, the French ran alongside Bellamy's craft and attempted to board.

It was a fierce hand-to-hand melee. The gallant French marines, with pike and cutlass, leaped onto the decks of the *Whydah* and soon gained control amidships. But the buccaneers were fighting to save their necks. One of Bellamy's men lit a bomb and tossed it in the midst of the advancing marines. The resultant explosion killed or wounded a score. Bellamy and his crew cut down the few dazed Frenchmen still left alive on the decks. The two ships drifted apart, exchanging shot for shot at point-blank range. The decks of both ships were slippery with blood. French marksmen and pirates, high up in the riggings, fought deadly duels with musket and pistols. The air was often rent by the screams of dying fighters as they fell seventy feet to the decks or plummeted into the sea. Twice the French boarded the *Whydah* only to be repulsed each time. Fate settled the contest. A cannon fired by a dying gunner on the pirate craft shattered the mainmast of the frigate. In a welter of splintered wood and torn sailcloth, the mast went overboard. The warship was a wreck, a derelict, unable to fight or flee. However, Bellamy and his rascals had had enough. the shocked and weary survivors were glad to sail away and back to their base on the Machias.

On the return of the *Mary Anne* and the snow with several prizes, the pirates again waxed brave. In April the fleet sailed from their river stronghold. At last they were on their way to sack the town of Newport.

With a fine breeze Black Sam's ship sailed down the coast, stopping long enough to capture a sturdy Dublin ship bound for New York. Aboard this prize was a rich cargo of whiskey and wine. Bellamy sent a crew aboard with orders to send a pleasing portion of the cargo to the *Whydah*.

Easier said than done! The hatches were sealed with heavy iron straps. After much labor the straps were removed only to discover a longboat lying atop the cargo. Eventually the men on the Dublin vessel were able to extract five bottles of wine and send them to Bellamy.

As the marauders' fleet neared Cape Cod, Paul Williams in the *Mary Anne* gave chase to a distant sail and became separated from the *Whydah*, the snow and the Dublin prize. Bellamy shortened sail and cruised slowly along the coast, waiting for his lieutenant to rejoin the fleet. Shortly before dark, the sloop *Fisher* of Nantucket unsuspectingly sailed into the midst of the pirate fleet and was captured without resistance. The master of the sloop was sent on board the *Whydah*.

Meanwhile, the sky was being overcast by threatening thunderheads. Far out to sea a thick fog began to form and soon obscured the horizon.

"Have ye an acquaintance with this coast?" Bellamy asked Robert Ingols, captain of the prize sloop *Fisher*. "Do ye know our position?"

"Aye! Ye are close by Nauset Island."

Evidently unable to make up his mind, Black Sam allowed his fleet to dawdle southward for another hour. There was scarcely a breath of wind, and the fog spread rapidly. Shortly after sunset the wind quartered and began to blow from the south, whipping away the fog and revealing to the startled pirates the sandy shores of Cape Cod only a mile to starboard.

Bringing his ship about, Bellamy reversed his course, faithfully followed by his consorts. At ten o'clock a terrific squall with winds of hurricane force swept from the east, blowing the pirate craft toward the shore.

"Can you save this ship?" Bellamy asked his captive. Captain Ingols nodded and took the helm. At that moment the buccaneers heard the angry roar of surf breaking on a shoal. Ingols ordered a stern anchor to be dropped overboard to halt the forward motion of the ship. A pirate with an axe in his hand stood by the taut anchor cable, ready to cut it when the bow of the vessel was brought around. Gradually Captain Ingols swung the head of the *Whydah* toward the northeast. For a few moments it appeared as if he would succeed in his desperate maneuver. However, the strain on the anchor cable was too great. It suddenly parted and the *Whydah* was hurled onto the reef.

Great waves broke over the ship. The main and mizzen masts snapped. In an instant the dying ship was covered with a shroud of wet canvas, cordage and spars. Like chips, the pirates were felled by the seas and swept overboard to drown in the surf. One hundred and forty-four men from the *Whydah* perished. Only two reached shore alive. The snow and one of the prizes were also washed ashore and wrecked. Into the churning surf of Cape Cod went dreams of a pirate kindgdom in New England.

Early the following morning inhabitants of the Cape found the bodies of the pirates scattered for miles along the sandy shore. Six survivors, battered and bruised by the surf, were captured and sent under guard to Boston, where they were subsequently tried, convicted, and hanged for their nefarious deeds.

One corpse, distinguished by a luxuriant black beard, was considered to be the mortal remains of Black Sam Bellamy and was buried as such.

Only two miles from the scene of the wreck of the *Whydah*, hidden in the dunes, was the home of the woman who had been forsaken by Black Sam. The few casual visitors who invaded her seclusion had noted the little mound, surmounted by a cross and shaded by pine trees, the grave of her child. After the wreck it was rumored that another grave had been dug in the pine grove, a large mound topped with a driftwood cross. In later years it was reputed to be the grave of Black Sam. What a strange twist of fate—Bellamy returning in death to the woman whom he had forsaken for the lure of gold.

What happened to Bellamy's treasure. Many treasure hunters have been convinced that the chest of coins, captured with the *Whydah*, had been buried somewhat near the pirate fort on the banks of the Machias River. Others are of the opinion that the chest was aboard the pirate craft when she was wrecked. To support this assumption is the fact that several coins have been found on the sandy beaches of Wellfleet.

Someday a well-equipped skin diver may locate the wreckage of the *Whydah* and find a treasure in a specie chest, a treasure of gold ducats, doubloons, guilders, pieces-of-eight, louis d'ors and fat English guineas.

Fear of Black Sam Bellamy and his cutthroat brethren forced the colonial governments to fit out and man well-armed cruisers to patrol the coastlines and protect coastal towns. The commanders of such vessels were answerable only to their respective governments. Some years later these colonial cruisers, the first American Navy, were of inestimable value in the capture of Louisburg in 1745.

The Iniquitous Captain Lightfoot

❦

When the brig *Maria* of Waterford, Ireland, anchored in Salem Harbor in 1819, she was in the hands of a group of mutineers. The captain of the ship reported to Salem authorities that when he had decided to make a landing at Halifax, one Michael O'Hanlon, a passenger, pointed a pistol at his head and threatened to kill him unless the *Maria* was sailed to a port in the United States. Several members of the crew sided with O'Hanlon. They seized the captain's guns, locked him in his cabin and forced the mate to navigate the ship to Salem.

The Irish vessel was crowded with immigrant passengers, many of them worn and sick from the long voyage. For this reason, the port officials quarantined the brig at once, allowing no one to set foot on shore. As the captain of the *Maria* was not injured by the mutineers but was released as soon as the ship reached port, the officials conveniently ignored the report of mutiny. Perhaps if they had had an inkling that Michael O'Hanlon was the famous Irish highwayman known as Captain Lightfoot, they might have been less complacent.

Michael O'Hanlon was only one of many aliases used by the robber. His true name was John Martin, of Connehy, Ireland. He was a handsome rogue with bright blue eyes, a fair complexion and a devil-may-care attitude which seemed to be irresistible to members of the fairer sex. His body was sturdy and compact, giving him an appearance of slightness despite his one hundred eighty-five pounds. He was quick-witted, agile and tremendously strong. It was claimed that he once killed a man with his bare fists. Although usually generous and good-natured, he was a creature of impulse, apt to become dangerous at any moment.

His criminal career began while he was quite young. In a tavern near his hometown, he became acquainted with the notorious highwayman known as Captain Thunderbolt. This knight of the road, taking a fancy to the young man, taught him the art of disguise and the finer points of highway robbery. Before many months passed, young Martin, by sheer daring, was exceeding the exploits of his more experienced tutor. After an episode in which he outran a company of the King's soldiers, he took the name of Captain Lightfoot. When robbing a stage-coach, he usually refused to take money or valuables from a lady, confining his depredations to the purses and jewelry of their male escorts. However, he sometimes exacted a kiss from the darlings as a toll for his magnanimity.

For two years this young marauder traveled the length and breadth of Ireland, often in the company of Captain Thunder-bolt, robbing and taking toll from all who used the King's highways. He had many women friends, some of them of social prominence, who were ever eager to hide him for a few days when he appeared to be in danger of capture.

Eventually Ireland became too hot for him. His deeds and description were posted in every hamlet and town, and there were many brave or foolhardy persons hunting him for the purpose of collecting the substantial rewards offered for him dead or alive.

Using the alias of Michael O'Hanlon, he bought passage on the *Maria*, describing himself as a laborer seeking employment in the United States. His seizure of the ship was typical of the man, for he could never for long keep from indulging in some act of villainy.

When the quarantine of the *Maria* was lifted, the Irish passengers were landed on the Crowninshield wharf. Here they were met by several gentlemen who wished to hire servants or laborers. Most of the immigrants took advantage of their offers. Michael O'Hanlon, however, refused to deal with them and headed for the nearest tavern. Here he stayed for a fortnight, spending his money on drink and women.

When his funds were depleted, Michael went to work for a Mr. Derby as a farmhand. For a period his work was satisfactory. The Derbys treated him well, giving him many little extras of clothing and food. After several weeks of good behavior, however, he gave way to his villainous impulses. He became drunk and forced his unwelcome attentions on his employer's daughter. When a fellow worker attempted to help the girl, Michael struck him a savage blow with a stick, knocking the man bleeding and unconscious to the ground. The girl escaped. When Mr. Derby heard of the affair, he promptly discharged the culprit.

Still using the name of Michael O'Hanlon, he secured another job as a brewery worker, but stayed only for a short time. Again he was fired for brawling. He left Salem and moved on to Portsmouth, New Hampshire, where he found work in a local brewery. While living in Portsmouth he received a legacy from his father's estate in Ireland. It was a considerable sum of money. Investing most of the funds in a small brewery, he worked industriously until it became a thriving enterprise. Again, after a period of effort, he returned to his spendthrift ways, spending large sums on liquor and loose women.

In the spring of 1821 Martin's business failed. Creditors attached his property, even seizing most of his clothing. For another month he stayed in Portsmouth, living with an enamored widow who showered him with gifts. Restlessness caused him to move on.

He hired a horse and chaise (his credit was still good) and drove to the village of Greenland where he visited a young girl whom he had one time promised to marry. He urged her to accompany him to Canada but she refused. Martin stayed with her until morning and then set off alone in his borrowed carriage toward the Canadian border.

His lack of money disturbed him. Shortly after crossing the Connecticut River into Vermont, he met a peddler's cart dawdling along the lonely, narrow road. The somnolent peddler was lolling back in his seat, allowing his horse to plot along at its own pace. On a sudden impulse Martin again became Captain Lightfoot, the highwayman. Driving his chaise in front of the cart, he pointed his pistol at the startled peddler.

"Sir! If you value your life, give me all your money," he demanded in a menacing tone.

When the frightened man made no move to comply with his demand, Martin leaped into the cart and struck him a savage blow in the face. The unconscious peddler fell heavily to the ground.

Captain Lightfoot searched the man and found a purse containing seventy dollars in his pocket. After counting the money, he mounted the chaise and drove toward the border.

When Martin arrived in Canada, he traveled a backwoods road to Quebec. Here he registered at an inn, using the name of Joseph Hendley. He sold the chaise and a few days later disposed of the horse. For them he received a total of thirty-two pounds.

With an adequate supply of money, he bought a sword-cane and another pistol, determined to continue his career as a highway robber. For a disguise he employed a tailor to make for him a suit of Quaker clothing.

One morning he left Quebec and walked along the highway

toward the settlement of Three Rivers. Under his arm he carried a bundle containing the Quaker suit. A few hours later two men riding in a calash toward Quebec saw a stranger kneeling in the center of the road, evidently in great pain. This was one of the clever subterfuges which had often been used by Captain Lightfoot in Ireland.

The driver of the calash reined in the horse, and the two men descended to help the sick or injured man. When they approached, Martin leaped to his feet. Pointing a pistol at the pair, he warned them in a stern voice to obey his instructions or suffer dire consequences. He relieved them of their purses and watches and told them to drive on.

The same day, this time dressed in the Quaker costume, he held up an old gentleman and stole his horse. A short time later he was disconcerted when a troop of Provincial Rangers almost captured him. Only by a breakneck dash through the woods was he able to evade them. He buried the Quaker suit, which was now a danger, let the stolen horse loose and made his way to Montreal on foot.

In Montreal he stayed for several days in a tavern frequented by thugs and thieves. His ready funds made him welcome. One night while in the city he tried to hold up a man on a darkened street. The stranger, however, proved to be his match. He struck Captain Lightfoot a severe blow on his gun arm with a club. The blow paralyzed his arm for a moment and he dropped his gun. His erstwhile victim continued to strike him until he was forced to flee. This was a humiliation which he had never before accepted from a single opponent.

After recovering from the beating, Martin decided to return to the United States. Leaving Montreal one morning, he walked along a wooded road toward Burlington. In quick succession he held up an Indian and a British soldier. The Indian resisted and the desperado shot him. He killed the soldier and took his horse, uniform and boots. A few days later, dressed in the soldier's uniform, he entered the secluded mansion of a wealthy landowner and spent the day terrorizing the master and his servants. He left after taking $170 in gold and silver coin from his unwilling host. A few miles from the mansion the rogue removed the soldier's uniform and tied it to the horse's saddle. He let the horse go and continued on foot toward the border. At one point he was stopped by Provincial Guards who were looking for the highwayman. He told a convincing story and they allowed him to cross the border. In Grand Isle he bought a fine saddle horse. Posing as a cattle dealer, he rode into Burlington and secured a room in a tavern.

However, the forces of justice were now relentlessly pursuing him. He was in an unknown country, without friends. His safety depended on the sagacity and experience gained in his career as Captain Lightfoot.

As he stood in the doorway of the tavern one evening, a horseman rode up. Mistaking him for the proprietor, the man handed him some handbills and requested that they be posted at once. After the rider left, Martin looked at the sheets in his hand. It was a disagreeable surprise to find that they contained a good description of him and the horse he had bought in Grand Isle, coupled with a reward of fifty pounds for his body —dead or alive. The authorities were closing in on him.

Martin destroyed the posters but soon discovered that others had been circulated throughout the area. Leaving Burlington, he took the road south. Twice he was recognized and forced to flee. Finally he tied his horse to a tree beside the highway and set out on foot to cross the mountains. Five days later he walked into Enfield, New Hampshire. The town had not heard of his depredations in Canada, and the people were friendly. Here he spent a few days in a quiet inn, resting after his long hike across the Green Mountains.

One fine morning Martin decided to walk to Concord. A full moon was shining, lighting up the road. A few miles from

Enfield he heard the sound of approaching horses. On an impulse he hid behind some bushes. A moment later he saw two men on horseback riding toward him. As they came abreast of his hiding place, one of them caught a glimpse of him.

"Who is there? Come out you rascal," the rider demanded.

Martin stepped from behind the bushes, his pistol pointing steadily at the horsemen.

"I am the bold Doherty from Scotland. You, my friends, must pay my fee. Give me your money or I'll ha' your blood."

Hastily, the two riders threw their purses on the ground.

"Now dismount!"

The two men obeyed, all the while begging the highwayman not to kill them. Martin forced them to lie face down on the ground. Then mounting one horse and leading the other, he rode away toward Concord. Unfamiliar with that section of New England, he lost his way. Finally he reached the Salisbury, New Hampshire, turnpike and decided to ride on to Newburyport.

Reaching Salisbury, he stayed overnight in a small tavern. Here he heard some talk of the Enfield robbery, but apparently no one suspected him. With foolhardy boldness he sold the two horses to a local farmer and a few minutes later stole a chaise from the hitching rack behind the meetinghouse. In this conveyance he rode to Newburyport.

Arriving in that thriving town without incident, he at once repaired to a large inn. He called himself Francis Bell and let it be known that he was a cattle dealer.

The next day he met a girl of good family whom he had known in Portsmouth and asked her to elope with him. She listened to his importunities and reluctantly consented. That evening he met the girl in front of her house, and they set out in the chaise for Salem. When they stopped at a tavern in Ipswich for refreshments, Martin overheard a drover telling the host that a sheriff was in Salem searching for a highway robber. This caused him to change his plans. Taking to lonely backwoods roads he drove to Beverly and secured a room in an obscure inn. The girl had no other recourse than to share his quarters. The next morning he informed her that business required him to leave her for a while. He rode to Salem, where discreet inquiries revealed that the sheriff had left the town. At a friend's house he spent several days drinking and carousing with a group of Irish immigrants. One morning he hitched up the chaise and set out for Boston. Spying a beautiful saddle horse tied up in front of a farmhouse, he deserted the chaise, stole the horse and continued toward Boston.

The Irish highwayman would have been less nonchalant if he had known that his proclivity for beguiling women had aroused the countryside. The parents and friends of the girl whom he had abandoned in the Beverly inn had posted his description and a reward for his arrest in every town and village in eastern Massachusetts. A short time after Captain Lightfoot had left Salem, a group of mounted officers set out on the turnpike for Boston. An erstwhile friend had betrayed him.

At this critical time the highwayman performed the most audacious robbery in his career. In broad daylight on the busy turnpike he held up Major Bray of Medford and took his purse and watch. As he was riding away from Bray's carriage, he was sighted by his pursuers from Salem. Instantly they spurred their horses toward him. Captain Lightfoot recklessly rode his horse through fields and woodlands and soon outdistanced the more cautious officers. After dark he boldly rode into Medford and stopped at a tavern. As he was dismounting, Major Bray came to the door and recognized him.

"The robber! The robber! Seize him!" the major shouted. Several mounted men in the courtyard galloped toward Martin. The Irishman swung his mount around and raced down a narrow lane and across a field. The animal was spent. When the fugitive tried to jump him across a wall, the horse halted so suddenly that his rider fell to the ground. Without a rider, the horse ran across the field, followed in the darkness by the pursuers.

Badly injured in the fall, Martin staggered away and managed to escape from the vicinity. Traveling at night and sleeping in the woods during the day, he reached the village of Holliston. Here he hid in a patch of brush near the main road where he was able to observe the activities around two farmhouses. He was hungry and ill and desperately in need of a horse to escape from the vicinity. His clothing, torn by his travels through woods and thickets, needed replacing.

In the evening the hunted man saw a farmer riding a trim chestnut mare stop at one of the houses and dismount. A youth unsaddled the animal, wiped it off with a handful of straw and led it into the barn. Captain Lightfoot decided to steal that mare come nightfall.

He waited patiently in the brush heap until near midnight before setting out toward the farm. All lights were out. Silence held sway. Martin stole to the barn and opened the door. In the darkness he fumbled along a wall until he found a saddle and a coat. He donned the coat at once. Holding the saddle in one hand he groped for the mare. Suddenly she neighed piercingly. He swung his hand around until his hand touched her shoulder. Desperately he fumbled for her bridle. Her heels clattered against the walls of the stall, creating a fearful racket. Martin finally threw the saddle on her back and cinched it. As he led her from the barn, a musket was fired almost in his face. Strong hands grabbed his coat and the cold barrel of a pistol was pressed against his head. Thus was Captain Lightfoot captured.

He was quickly identified as the man who had robbed Major Bray and was immediately taken to the jail at Lechmere Point in Cambridge.

On the ninth day of October, John Martin, alias Captain

Lightfoot, was tried in open court. Convicted of highway robbery, he was sentenced to die by hanging. The sheriff placed him in close confinement with shackles on his hands and legs.

One day when the turnkey entered the cell, he found Martin groaning in pain. The prisoner said that he was ill and asked the official to fasten a shawl over his shoulders. As the kindly man adjusted the shawl, Martin dropped his pewter cup. The turnkey bent over to pick it up. Martin raised his manacled hands and struck him a terrific blow, knocking him to the floor. He took the official's keys and unlocked the handcuffs but could not find the keys to his leg shackles. Then picking up the leg weights, he hobbled down the prison corridor and threw his weight against a wooden door which stood between him and freedom. The turnkey revived and began to call for help. People in the street outside the prison took up the cry and the alarm became general. Guards rushed into the corridor and overpowered the desperate man. After the attempted jailbreak, John Martin asked for a priest.

On the day of execution, Captain Lightfoot was placed in a carriage surrounded by several deputies on horseback and followed by a cart containing his coffin. When he arrived at the gallows, Martin climbed to the platform without assistance. For a few minutes he gazed down on the large multitude gathered there to see him die. The sheriff read the death warrant. Martin said a short prayer and stood up.

"I am ready," he said firmly. Untying his neckerchief, he assisted in fixing the fatal noose about his neck. He then took a handkerchief and, after the death cap had been placed over his face, asked when he should drop it.

The sheriff answered, "When you please."

Martin slowly raised his hand thrice to his breast as in prayer, then dropped the handkerchief. Instantly he was launched into eternity—the last man in New England to hang for highway robbery.

LEGENDS OF PLACE NAMES,

OF A BOUNDARY BATTLE,

A DEADLY FEUD,

AN UNFAITHFUL LOVER

AND A TARDY BRIDEGROOM.

Bride's Brook

Many years ago, Bride's Brook received its name when it figured in a boundary dispute which was finally settled in a most unusual manner.

The story began on a warm day in early spring. A young Puritan of New London, who had successfully wooed the daughter of a neighboring landowner, set forth with his betrothed with the intention of getting married. According to the laws of that period, only a magistrate could tie the bonds of matrimony.

The happy couple walking a woodland path toward the town center of New London came to the west bank of a brook which was running deep and wide due to recent rains. As they stood in consternation, casting about for some means of crossing the swollen stream without injury to their wedding finery, they were hailed by a stranger who appeared on the opposite bank.

"My friends! Is there a boat or bridge nearby where I might cross this stream dryshod?" he asked.

The young Puritan shook his head in despair. "Nay, I know of none. Sara and I were on our way to town to get married, but it looks as if we must wait a day for the water to subside."

The stranger laughed at his doleful expression. "Stay, good

sir! I am Governor Winthrop, magistrate of New London. I can marry thee if you will find a witness. It would be most inconvenient to postpone thy plans."

The young man gave a shout of joy. After a hasty word to his Sara, he hurried back up the path. In a short time he returned with a local farmer who had consented to act as a witness to the ceremony.

Thus the couple were married. After the brief ceremony the happy pair hurried to a new house which had been erected for them by friends and neighbors. There they received felicitations from their neighbors.

Several days later, at a town meeting in Lyme, a question was raised concerning the authority of Governor Winthrop, a freeman of New London, to perform a wedding on land claimed by the township of Lyme. Authorities of that town stated that it was their belief that the boundary between the two settlements was the Nehantic River, which was some distance east of the brook. The freemen of Lyme then decided that Governor Winthrop had exceeded his authority.

This ruling placed a shocking interpretation on the marriage performed by the side of the brook. If the couple had not been legally married, they now were living in sin. A group of conscientious settlers hurried to the bridegroom's house, explained the situation and separated the young man and his Sara. The tearful bride was conducted to the home of her parents and left in their custody.

On the following morning the angry young bridegroom hurried into the town of New London, made representation to the authorities on the injustice he had suffered and urged them to take some action about the affair. The town fathers assured him that the east bank of the brook in question was the correct boundary between the two settlements; consequently, the governor had been within his legal rights in performing a wedding ceremony. Their promises of action, however, were vague and lacked enthusiasm.

That same evening the still angry young Puritan walked into his father-in-law's house and carried Sara back to his home, threatening to shoot anyone who tried to invade their privacy.

In the dilemma created by this action by the brash young man, the elders of Lyme decided to bestir themselves. A committee was appointed and hustled to New London in an attempt to settle the boundary question. However, the New Londoners refused to arbitrate. They insisted that the western boundary of their settlement was the brook—which for the first time was referred to as Bride's Brook. The Lyme committee returned home to confess their failure.

A suggestion that the two settlements allow the court at Hartford to decide the question was rejected by both sides. Neither of them wished to pay the expenses such a course would entail. Someone advanced a proposal that champions be picked to represent each town and that they engage in fistic combat to decide the vexatious question of the boundary. Both New London and Lyme had bold, brawny lads ready to fight for a cause. Gravely the authorities of the two settlements agreed to abide by the results of such a fight. They shook hands on it.

New London selected two champions by the names of Picket and Latimer while Lyme committed its cause to two men named Griswold and Ely. On the appointed day a goodly crowd gathered at the scene of the battle. The four men had their adherents who made it a matter of pride to support them vocally. I'll wager that a few Puritan misses found places where they could unobtrusively watch the battle. Speaking of wagers, I wonder if many bets were placed on the contest by the freemen of the two towns.

The battle was fierce and bloody. The four champions gave their followers plenty to cheer about. Finally Ely punished his opponent so badly that the man was unable to continue. Minutes later, Griswold vanquished his foe. The contest was over and Lyme had won. Thereafter, the boundary was considered to be the Nehantic River.

A short time after the battle, a crestfallen young Puritan and his Sara appeared before Griswold, the Lyme magistrate, and were duly and truly married.

Chocorua Mountain

Looming over the wooded hills in the intervals, on the southern approach to the White Mountains, the rugged, barren peak of Chocorua Mountain dominates the countryside. The summit is a huge cap of gray granite, devoid of vegetation. Below is a wilderness of ledges and steep ravines and a mass of coniferous trees struggling grimly for the nutriments in the meager soil. A crystal clear lake, like a diamond set in the emerald grasslands at the base of the mountain, reflects the wild beauty of the scene. This body of water is named Chocorua Lake. Mountain and lake are memorials to a great Indian chief.

Chocorua was a sachem of the Sokokis, an Indian tribe which claimed northern New Hampshire and the Maine borderlands as their hunting grounds. Once the Sokokis had been a numerous people, but white man's diseases and white man's rum had decimated them. Despite many provocations, they remained friendly with the English settlers on the Massachusetts and New Hampshire frontiers.

In the early 1700s Chocorua, although still a young man, had been touched by joy and sorrow. He had married White Fawn, a beautiful maiden of the Ossipee tribe, and in the fullness of time she bore him a sturdy son.

As the years passed, the boy grew tall and strong. His playground was the wild slopes of the mountain and the shores of the crystal lake. Under the guidance of his father he became proficient in the use of bow and arrow and the fish spear. He learned the art of stalking moose and deer and contrived ingenious snares to capture waterfowl. Often he contributed fish and meat to the aged and less agile members of the tribe. These were days of happiness, peace and plenty in the Indian lodges in the intervales.

Then death in the form of virulent smallpox raced through the encampments of the Sokokis, silencing laughter with cold fingers. Among the many who died was Chocorua's lovely squaw, White Fawn.

The chieftain's lodge on the banks of the shimmering lake became a place of sorrow. Chocorua and his son, their hearts filled with grief, went through the customary motions of living, but the valley which had once appeared to be a segment of paradise, now seemed bare and bleak. In an attempt to assuage their sorrow, father and son left their lodge and traveled into the fastnesses of the White Mountains to hunt and fish. Here they abided until spring touched grass and twigs with green.

Returning to their lodge, they were surprised to observe smoke rising from the chimney of a white man's cabin across the lake. It had been erected in their absence. From the medicine men and councilors of the tribe, Chocorua learned that the stranger had entered the valley accompanied by a woman and a boy. The younger warriors of the tribe, angered by the intrusion and fearful that other whites might follow, were plotting to wipe out the little household and burn the cabin.

Chocorua advised the warriors not to take such drastic action and urged them to be patient. Later he went in person to visit the interlopers. The newcomers were named Campbell. They were friendly and hospitable. Chocorua stayed at their home until darkness hung a curtain over the intervales.

Cornelius Campbell, accompanied by his son, returned the visit. From then on, Chocorua and the Campbells were friends. Often the Sokokis' chieftain would leave a haunch of venison or a brace of ducks at the Campbell cabin. The white man would reciprocate with gifts of salt, corn bread or bits of hard sugar.

Chocorua's son began to visit the cabin, and Mrs. Campbell treated him like a member of her family. She made him a gay pair of deerskin moccasins and a soft, tanned hunting shirt. He grew accustomed to sitting at the table and eating with his white friends. He was particularly fond of the wild strawberry jam made by Mrs. Campbell. Frequently she would fill a small crock with this delicacy and leave it on the table for the ever hungry boys.

The Indian boy played and hunted with young Campbell, who was of the same age. He taught him how to stalk deer, how to build fish weirs to catch the swift brook trout, how to construct snares for rabbits and birds. The boys became constant companions.

In those days the mountain intervales with their many lakes and streams were excellent hunting grounds. In season geese and crane, ducks and pigeons would arrive in flocks to add their numbers to the native population of grouse and quail. Deer, moose and bear were abundant, and there was no scarcity of rabbits, beaver and other small game. However, the lands were becoming increasingly infested with many packs of timber wolves which preyed on the wildlife, even posing a threat to dogs, wandering Indian children and unwary hunters.

Cornelius Campbell, after one of his dogs had been killed by a pair of the gray marauders, determined to make war on them. Relentlessly he hunted them and set dozens of traps and deadfalls in their favorite haunts with some degree of success, but the efforts were too slow and time-consuming. Finally he decided to poison pieces of meat and leave them near the dens where the wolves would be sure to find them. He mixed a deadly batch of poison in a small crock. Unfortunately he left it on the table in the cabin while he was outside assisting his wife in making lye.

Fate decreed that Chocorua's son should enter the cabin at that time. The boy called but the busy Campbells did not hear him. On the table was a crock, presumably filled with delicious strawberry jam. He took a large swallow of the poison before discovering his mistake. Soon after, he became violently ill. Cornelius Campbell found him writhing in pain on the floor. Sorrowfully and tenderly the white man carried the boy to the Sokokis' encampment. Tribal medicine men did all they could to save his life, but in vain. That night Chocorua's son died. The chieftain had been hunting in the big lake country to the east. He knew nothing of the tragedy until he returned to his lodge.

In the agony of his sorrow, Chocorua blamed the Campbells for the death of his son. He determined to make the white man suffer loss. Let him savor the bitterness of the death of loved ones.

Early one morning Chocorua arrived near the Campbell cabin and concealed himself behind some brush. Patiently he waited until the white man left his home and disappeared into the forest. After Cornelius had been gone for several minutes, the chief emerged from his hiding place and ran to the cabin. Mrs. Campbell was sewing a hunting jacket when he entered. With crazed savagery Chocorua tomahawked her. Hearing the noise, the young Campbell boy entered the room and in a trice was stretched lifeless on the floor. Leaving the blood-stained cabin with its pitiful inmates, the Indian returned to his lodge, knowing well that the white man, when he discovered his loss, would pursue him relentlessly.

Dusk was falling over the intervals when Cornelius Campbell returned to his cabin. He stopped at the edge of the clearing. The house which he had built with so much pride appeared dark and forbidding. No column of smoke showed above the mud and wattle chimney. No gleam of candlelight beamed through the oil-paper window panes. A sense of apprehension gripped him. He broke into a run and dashed into the house. Mercifully darkness hid some of the bloody details. His shriek of anguish carried across the lake. Chocorua heard it, but the sound aroused no satisfaction in his heart. Too well the tortured cry echoed his own feeling of heartbreaking loss. He had intended to ambush and kill the white man. Now revenge was ashes in his mouth. Spreading a blanket on the floor of the lodge, he heaped on it his rifle, bow, knife, a quiver of arrows, all of his prized possessions. On top of the pile he laid the gay moccasins which Mrs. Campbell had given to his son. For many minutes he stood like a bronze statue, staring down at the heap on the blanket. Mementos and weapons—they represented his life's cycle. Finally, with stately strides, he left the lodge, carrying with him nothing but the paddle of a canoe.

On the banks of the lake he launched his birch bark craft and paddled away in the darkness toward the base of the mountain. When he arrived on the opposite shore, the first tinges of dawn began to light the eastern sky. He pushed the canoe out into the water and began to ascend the rocky slope. Several times he slipped on dew-drenched rocks, but continued until he reached the topmost peak. He stood there for a long time, surveying the panorama of mountains and woodlands. This was his country.

After a while he descended to the edge of a steep cliff near the trail and seated himself on a granite boulder. Far below, spruce and fir trees were toylike in the distance. The sun climbed high in the heavens, reflecting its hot rays on the naked rock, but Chocorua sat quietly. Now and then he scanned the trail below which led up to his aerie. The sun was sinking in the west when he saw movement on the trail. Cornelius Campbell was climbing the mountain toward him, seeking his life.

The white man climbed fast. Blinded by his exertions, he did not see the chieftain of the Sokokis until he reached the top of the cliff. It was then that the Indian stood up and faced him. For several heartbeats, the two men confronted each other on the narrow edge of the precipice. Hate reacted first. Campbell raised his musket and fired. Chocorua, mortally wounded, gave a defiant scream and leaped from the cliff. The white man watched him until his body disappeared in the woods far below.

What happened afterward? Perhaps it was vertigo. Perhaps he tripped. No one will ever know. Hunters of the Sokokis found Cornelius Campbell's battered body only a few yards away from the remains of their chieftain. Legend claims that both were buried on the shore of beautiful Lake Chocorua.

Nancy's Brook

🌢

This is a tale of the cupidity and deceitfulness of a man and the love and courage of a woman. It began and ended in the White Mountains of New Hampshire.

In 1797 the township of Jefferson, high on the slopes of Mount Starr King, was bought in its entirety by Colonel Joseph Whipple, a wealthy and prominent man in New Hampshire affairs.

The great stands of trees in the township were a source of wealth untapped. Colonel Whipple built roads, erected sawmills and a forge. He employed woodcutters, sawyers, a blacksmith and a wheelwright. On one of the choicest sections of land in Jefferson, he built a large mansion flanked by two immense barns. He hired two domestics, Deborah Vickers and an Irish girl named Nancy, to work in the household. Here he lived in the style of an old country baronet.

Nancy was a pretty girl with a pleasing personality who endeared herself to everyone in Jefferson by her gentle kindness. All of the eligible bachelors in the township fell in love with her at one time or another, but they courted her in vain. She remained heart-free. Cheerfully and energetically she performed her tasks about the house, an exemplary paragon of a housekeeper. At her request Colonel Whipple saved her wages, giving her an accounting every twelve months. She worked three years for the Colonel, happy and contented in his household until . . .

One day a young man serving a sentence in Rochester for counterfeiting escaped from jail and sought refuge in the mountains. After many days of wandering, he was found starving, sick and destitute by woodcutters working for Whipple. They carried him to the Colonel's house, where he was placed in bed. Nancy was appointed to nurse him back to health.

The youth was tall, handsome and well educated, possessing the social graces of a man of the world. Nancy fell in love with him but managed to conceal her feelings. On the other hand, he treated her with light affection but with none of the deeper nuances of true love. When he regained his strength, the young man accepted a job as bookkeeper for the Colonel and continued to live in the Whipple house.

However, he was an unprincipled rogue. He was used to a life of travel and excitement. The prospect of living for any appreciable length of time in the rustic atmosphere of a frontier village was unbearable to him. Nevertheless, he realized that his security from arrest was assured as long as he remained away from the larger towns.

As the days went by, Nancy, under the strain of living near her beloved but forced to conceal her love for him, became thin and wan. Her infectious good humor became less and less evident.

One day while studying the Colonel's accounts, the new bookkeeper noticed that Nancy was credited with a large sum of money for back wages. He questioned her and learned that the money was not held in trust. She could obtain it from the Colonel upon request.

Instantly his villainy suggested a way to rob the girl. Pretending that he was falling in love with her (which was certainly not a difficult task), he courted her at every opportunity. On the last day of October he asked her to marry him. Nancy, her heart overflowing with love and joy, answered him with all the eloquence of a girl in love. The couple set the date for the wedding. It would be on the twenty-eighth day of November. A brief honeymoon would be spent in Portsmouth.

On the surface it appeared to be an uncommonly happy love match. Colonel Whipple gave the couple his blessing. Fellow workers enjoyed their shy behavior and embellished every meeting with bucolic and rude attempts of humor which were greeted with blushes and smiles by the happy pair. When the date of the wedding drew near, Nancy asked the Colonel for her money. With many expressions of felicitations, the good man counted out her wages in "hard" money, placed it in a linen pouch and gave it to her. As a wedding present, Whipple also gave her a small, gold brooch rimmed with pearls. Nancy thanked him with tears in her eyes and ran to show the exquisite piece of jewelry to her lover.

The rascally bookkeeper's eyes grew wide when he saw the pouch of silver coins and the lovely brooch. "You should buy a new dress for our wedding," he told her. "One of the lumber wagons will be leaving early tomorrow morning for Lancaster. The driver is Will Pease. Ride in with him. Take five dollars with you to buy a fine dress. I will hold the balance of the money until you return."

She trusted him implicitly and handed over the pouch of silver without question. When the lumber wagon left Jefferson the next morning for Lancaster, Nancy was seated on the wide board bench beside the driver. Colonel Whipple, riding a swift little Narragansett, saluted her as he trotted off toward Portsmouth where he was to serve in the legislature.

The bookkeeper spent the morning conversing with a groom and mending the heel of a boot. At midday he ate a leisurely lunch with the cook, Deborah Vickers. Going to his room, he packed his belongings and emptied the pouch of silver coins into his pocket. He paused briefly to admire the gold brooch before placing it with the coins. No one noticed him leaving the house. Without undue haste he walked along the trail toward Crawford Notch. He was rid of his self-imposed prison in Jefferson. With Nancy's money in his pocket he would enjoy life in the bustling town of Portsmouth. As he walked along the trail, the sky became overcast. A cold brisk wind from the northeast began to whip through the trees. Snowflakes began to fall, spreading a white carpet over the ground.

When Nancy arrived in Lancaster, she immediately hurried to the general store. From the store's scanty stock she selected a blue dress, ornamented by a white collar and shining pewter buttons. It was lovely. After paying for the dress, she had nearly a dollar left. She bought a pair of pewter buckles for her lover and left the store.

At Nancy's request the friendly driver hurried to unload the wagon, and they started back to Jefferson. It was early twilight when they arrived in the big yard behind the Whipple mansion. Snow had been falling for some time, the wind hurling the flakes like soft, white bullets. The happy girl, her wedding dress over her arm, ran into the house. She could hardly wait to show it to her intended husband. She would bewitch him in this beautiful dress.

She called his name as she hurried from room to room, but there was no reply. A quick search proved that he was not in the front of the house. Deborah Vickers, who had been in the kitchen all day, had not seen him since lunchtime. Nancy ran through the snow to the barns, expecting to find him chatting with the groom or one of the woodcutters who sometimes slept there. He had not been seen all afternoon. As she walked back to the house, disturbed over her betrothed's absence, she met a woodchopper, his jacket covered with snow.

"This is not the kind of weather for a little doe like you to go walking around in," he said to her.

Her voice quavering with fear, she asked him if he had seen the bookkeeper.

The woodcutter nodded. "I met your intended going through the Notch only a few hours ago. He told me that he was going to Portsmouth to make arrangements for your wedding."

Nancy hurried to her lover's room. All of his belongings were gone—as if he never expected to return. On the floor, quite empty, was the money pouch which had held her wages. What her thoughts were, no one can say. She told Deborah Vickers that she was leaving for Portsmouth and marched out into the blizzard. Deborah tried to stop her, but Nancy would not listen.

Two hours later the stableman came into the kitchen, his coat caked with snow. Deborah told him about Nancy's departure, and he hurried back to the barn where several woodcutters were waiting out the storm. They organized a search party and plowed through the snow toward Crawford Notch. Visibility was limited to a few feet. Twice the men lost their way in the howling storm.

In the Notch was a small cabin, used as a shelter by travelers. Here the search party found evidence that Nancy had reached the place. The ashes in the fireplace contained live coals, and a linen pouch, wet and limp, lay on the floor. But the girl had gone on. It was senseless to continue the search in the dark. The men built a roaring fire and waited in the cabin until dawn.

Early the next morning the storm abated. The search party left the comfortable cabin and trudged south through the deep snow in the mountain pass. Beside a storm-swollen brook, which would forever after bear her name, they found Nancy. She was huddled against a huge boulder, her body nearly covered with snow. The exhausted girl had found her strength unequal to the task of crossing the swift waters. She had dropped beside the stream and had frozen to death. Clutched in her hands was a pair of pewter buckles.

The searchers carried her mortal remains back to Jefferson. There she was buried.

It was said later that the thief and errant lover did not long enjoy the fruits of his crime. In a waterfront dive in Portsmouth, he was beaten and robbed. His skull was fractured by the blows he received. Soon afterward he became insane. His last days were spent beating against the iron doors of an insane asylum.

This is probably the best known of the many legends of the White Mountains. At the time of this story Benning Wentworth was royal governor of New Hampshire.

Hasty Corners

In the town of Scituate, Rhode Island, where it borders the town of Foster, there is a network of old dirt roads which once served a thriving community. In colonial times this area was loosely known by such names as Hopkinsville, Cider Town and Whip-o-will Heights. A crossing of two of these roads is called Hasty Corners. In the 1700s it was a well-known place, graced by the presence of a small church, a tavern and a store.

Shortly before the Revolutionary War a farmer named John Hopkins owned an interest in the tavern, was a deacon of the church and also served as a constable of the town of Scituate. His farm was on a large tract of land adjacent to the Corners. He had been blessed with four children.

The oldest was a girl of sixteen named Patience. She was a pretty and talented young lady. However, her disposition belied her name, for she was both quick-tempered and headstrong.

Neighbors of the Hopkins's were the family of Amos Barden, a farmer who possessed a large herd of cows and produced butter and cheese for the Providence market.

Amos Barden's son Matthew, a stalwart young man, was the recognized sweetheart of Patience. He was her escort at husking bees and musket shoots and visited her at home at least once a week. Folks figured that it would be only a matter of time before the couple posted banns of marriage.

The battle of Lexington and Concord changed many routines in New England. Matthew Barden, with most of the young men of Scituate, marched to Cambridge to join the rapidly growing Continental Army. They took potshots at the Redcoats, helled around some, and when the British finally evacuated Boston, they disbanded.

Matthew returned home to find that in his absence Patience had been courted by a local cattle dealer named Alfred Luther. Impetuous Matthew called on Mr. Luther and advised him to stay away from the Hopkins house.

The cattle dealer, a big, hulking, red-faced man, was not impressed. He told young Barden to mind his own business. These unfriendly words led to fisticuffs. In the ensuing brawl Matthew was trounced.

This defeat should have caused the youth to pause for reflection, but, as noted before, he was impetuous. He called on Patience and demanded her assurance that she would never allow Luther to visit her again. Foolish youth! These were words to set an independent-minded young lady abalking. In no uncertain terms she informed him that he had no claims on her; furthermore, she would see whom she pleased whenever she pleased. She also intimated that Alfred Luther was a gentleman while he was a ruffian.

Completely chastened, Matthew again left home to join the army.

Three long years went by. Once every week Alfred Luther called on Patience and begged her to be his wife, but the girl seemingly could not make up her mind. Finally John Hopkins resolved the stalemate. He told his daughter that she must either marry Luther or send him packing, pointing out to her that at nineteen she was an old maid. The next time Luther called, Patience agreed to become his wife. They set the date for the wedding on the first Saturday in September.

One day Major Matthew Barden returned home from the war. He had been wounded at Yorktown. He created some attention when he arrived at the Corners. He was a splendid figure in the blue and buff uniform of a Continental regular. His epaulets shone like gold as he rode up to the tavern. A friend told him of the impending wedding of Patience Hopkins and Alfred Luther. He made no comment.

The next day he rode over to the Hopkins house to pay his respects to his neighbors. Patience met him at the door. They talked together for a long while. After he left, the bride-to-be appeared unusually sad and pensive.

Meanwhile, plans for the wedding went on apace. John Hopkins wanted to make it a memorable affair. The time was set for twelve thirty, and a well-known minister from Pawtucket agreed to wed the couple. A whole ox was to be roasted in a large pit behind the church, and rum and cider in casks and barrels were stored in the tavern to quench the thirst of menfolk who always find weddings to be thirsty events. The women of the neighborhood had promised to bake cakes, pies and sweetmeats for the hungry crowd that would surely attend. The corner lot between the church and the tavern was to be festooned with hanging decorations and filled with sawhorse tables. It was expected to be a gala affair.

Whip-o-will Heights seethed with activities and expectations until the appointed day arrived. The farmers and their families began to arrive early at the Corners. Girls gathered like a flock of chicks around the tables, ostensively to help their mothers set up for the party. Yet their eyes often strayed toward a group of young bloods who wrestled and played pranks in front of the tavern. The weather cooperated. It was a sunny yet cool day.

Just before noon the minister arrived from Pawtucket and

alighted from his horse in front of the church. He was greeted by John Hopkins, who directed him to the store where he could rest and refresh himself in privacy.

A little later, Patience Hopkins arrived at the church with her bridesmaid and a large retinue of female relations and well-wishers. Self-consciously they stood before the door of the church. They were soon joined by Matthew Barden and two of his cousins, youths of his own age, all dressed in their finest. They were evidently in a gay mood, laughing and joking together. A crowd of youngsters gathered around to watch the wedding party.

A few minutes before noon John Hopkins crossed the green and greeted his daughter. They whispered together for a moment. He then entered the church, followed by many of the country folk.

Suddenly Matthew, in a loud voice, asked Patience if she had changed her mind and was willing to marry a real soldier. The girl gave him a glance of scorn but refused to answer. The time appointed for the ceremony was near, and as yet the bridegroom had not arrived at the church. The minister stepped from the store and walked across the green toward the group in front of the church.

"It looks as if Al Luther is not going to show up for his wedding," one of Barden's companions said aloud.

"We will have a wedding," Barden said with a laugh. "Patience Hopkins will wait till sundown for her betrothed; she's that anxious to spend his money."

Patience pressed her lips together angrily. "If Alfred Luther does not appear in three minutes, there will be no wedding," she announced grimly.

Then a sequence of events took place so rapidly that the onlookers were stunned. A trembling little man carrying a large book and escorted by two husky youths hurried to the group in front of the church door. Matthew took the bride-to-be by the arm. One of Matthew's cousins shut the church door and leaned against it. The trembling little man sat down on the church steps and opened the big book. One of his escorts produced a quill and a jar of ink. Matthew handed the quill to Patience.

"Sign here," he commanded.

Without any visible hesitation, she signed her name in the book. Matthew placed his signature on the line below. Taking the girl's hand he faced the minister.

"We are ready. Please proceed with the ceremony."

"Is this the man you intend to marry?" asked the surprised cleric.

He took an almost indiscernible nod as his answer. At this, the good man smiled expansively.

"Fine!" he exclaimed. "Let us all enter the church."

"No! We will be married here," young Barden said firmly.

So the dumfounded minister married Patience Hopkins to Matthew Barden on the steps of the church while her father, relatives and neighbors waited inside to witness a ceremony which was to have united Patience Hopkins and Alfred Luther.

After the pastor had given his blessing and while Matthew was kissing the bride, the church door flew open before the charge of an irate John Hopkins. At the same moment a bedraggled figure came running across the green. It was the absent bridegroom Alfred Luther, his fine broadcloth suit covered with dirt, leaves and cobwebs.

"Arrest those men," he shouted, waving a hand toward Matthew and his cousins.

John Hopkins ignored him. The farmer's angry countenance was scowling at the wedding party.

"What in thunder is going on here?" he demanded. "Why are you not in the church?"

"They locked me in the outhouse behind the tavern," Alfred Luther moaned.

"Father! Matthew and I have just been married," Patience informed her parent.

The poor man looked bewildered. "How could you—without banns or clerk?"

Matthew pointed to the little man with the big book. "The town clerk is here. Patience and I are registered in the book. The banns have been posted on the church door for seven days. You've been too busy to notice them."

John Hopkins shook his head. "Hasty! You youngsters acted all-fired hasty. But you are not going to spoil this day. March right into church and get married over again—this time in front of our neighbors."

"How about me?" Alfred Luther asked in an anguished voice.

The farmer looked at him pityingly. "Kind a looks like you got here a mite late," he commented. "This is a hasty place—yes, a pretty hasty place."

INDIAN LEGENDS:

STRANGE TALES OF THE

ORIGIN OF CORN,

OF A MYSTERIOUS GEM,

OF A MAIDEN'S LOVE

AND THE FORMATION OF

MANITOU'S MOUNTAINS.

The Story of Mon-do-min

Mon-do-min, ancient warrior and hunter of the great Wampanoag nation, sat alone in his lodge on the banks of the Nemasket River. He was old and lame and could no longer hunt the wild deer and the bear. He had not tasted food for many days. Crouching over his warm hearth, he dreamed of days long ago when he had been a great hunter and his lodge was well stocked with meat.

Outside his shelter the night was cold and stormy. Keche No-din, Spirit of the Wind, wailed and moaned through the trees and reached through cracks into the lodge to whip little tongues of flame from the glowing coals on the hearth. In the glowing coals, Mon-do-min saw the face of Shah-wain-ne-me-shin, the Great Spirit. The old man bowed his head and prayed aloud.

"Oh, Shah-wain-ne-me-shin, have pity on me. Send me food that I may not die of hunger."

Even as he ceased speaking, came a gust of wind through the doorway, and a bird hurtled into the lodge and fell fluttering at his feet. It was a fat partridge. Happily the old man dressed the bird and laid it on the hearth to cook.

Presently, amid the pauses of the wind, Mon-do-min heard cries of distress. It was a woman's voice. Bravely the old warrior left his lodge and stumbled out into the freezing storm. He found the woman kneeling beside a rock. She had wandered from her lodge and become lost in the storm. The cold wind had numbed her until she could scarcely walk.

With all his waning strength, Mon-do-min helped her into the shelter of his home. He placed a warm beaver robe over her shoulders and rubbed her limbs until circulation returned to her benumbed body. Taking the partridge from the hearth, he offered it to her.

"My sister!" he said. "This is a bird that the Great Spirit has given to me. Take it and eat. It will strengthen thee. I am old and weary and must die. This is as the Great Spirit wishes. Remember me when you see anyone alone and hungry. Give to them as I have given to you. Farewell! I shall not see you again until we meet in the Country of Souls."

Mon-do-min said no more. He wrapped his old body in a robe and turned his face from the hearth. That night, Shah-wain-ne-me-shin took him to his great lodge in the Country of Souls.

In the morning the woman awoke from her slumber. From her bed she saw Mon-do-min dead on the floor of the lodge. Then she arose and returned to her village. She told the sachems of the Wampanoag of the generosity of the old hunter. Warriors went to his lodge. They wrapped his body in skins and burried him on the banks of the river.

When the Moon of Leaves (June) spread warmth over the land, Indian hunters discovered that the ground around Mon-do-min's lodge was covered with fine, dark green shoots. It was like grass only the leaves were broader and waved like banners in the sun. They told their people and a great crowd gathered to see this wonder. And as they stood there on the banks of the Nemasket River, the Great Spirit spoke to them from a dark cloud overhead.

"My children!" he said. "Listen to what I say to you. This

that you see shall be food for you to eat when it ripens into full ears of grain. It shall be called Mon-do-min [corn]. It shall bear his name to remind you of his great kindness to the poor and helpless. And you shall tell this story to your children, and your children's children, and to all the nations. Give thanks to Mon-do-min when you see his green leaves waving like banners by the Lake of White Stones [Assawampsett Lake] and the river of the Nemaskets."

The Serpent of Carbuncle Hill

Years ago, in what is now Coventry, Rhode Island, there lived a huge serpent. Its den was on a ridge known as Carbuncle Hill. There is no clue to the species of this reptile. Set in the center of its head was a great gem carbuncle, bright red and glowing with the radiance of fire.

The Indians feared this creature as an evil spirit and tried to placate it with offerings of meat and fish. In this manner they were successful for a long time. Meanwhile, the snake grew larger and stronger year by year. Finally, in the pride of its strength, it attacked a village near the Pawtuxet River, killing many of the Indians and carrying away the daughter of the village sachem. Terrified, the villagers appealed to the twin chiefs of the Narragansetts for assistance.

The Narragansetts quickly assembled a large war party and invaded the land of the serpent. They found the creature at the base of Carbuncle Hill and attacked it with arrows, spears and stone axes. The battle was long and bloody. Many of the Indian warriors were slain before the evil reptile was subdued and killed.

They found the torn body of the Indian girl in the serpent's den. The carbuncle was cut from the snake's head and given to the grieving sachem of the Pawtuxet Indians.

Years went by. The famous carbuncle remained in the tribe. It possessed unusual properties. On the approach of danger, the gem would glow brilliantly, thus warning the tribesmen.

When white men landed on the shores of Rhode Island, they heard of this wonderous gem. Many a settler wished to possess it, but the Indians guarded it jealously.

Time went by and the white settlements spread along the coast and rivers. The white men became numerous. It was then that they decided to take the carbuncle from the Indians. Secretly organizing an expedition, they left the settlements and marched along Indian trails toward the Pawtuxet encampment. They hoped to surprise the Indians, but the glowing carbuncle gave warning, and the natives were ready for the fray.

The Indians ambushed the white army and inflicted many casualties on them. The battle raged long and savagely. At last, only the Indian sachem and five of the white men were still alive and unwounded. Trying to escape, the Indian fled to the banks of a nearby pond and concealed himself in a thicket. Unfortunately the glow of the carbuncle attracted the attention of one of his pursuers. Creeping close, this man aimed his musket and fired. The sachem, mortally wounded, staggered from his hiding place. Swinging his arm, he gave a mighty toss. The wonderous carbuncle, like a live red coal, arched over the water and sank with a splash in the center of the pond—thus lost forever from the sight of men.

Wahconah

Many years ago, the warlike Mohawks crossed the Housatonic River and conquered the Algonquin tribes to the east. The few Housatonic Indians left alive after the invasion were looked upon as cowards and weaklings by the conquerors and were treated with contempt. Pleased with the sylvan valleys and pleasant woodlands, many of the Mohawks remained and built a fortified town on the banks of a sweetwater creek.

One of the sachems of these Mohawks was Decanawida, a brave warrior, noted for his wisdom and reverence for the Great Spirit. In his lodge lived a young daughter named Wahconah, whose grace, beauty and friendliness endeared her to everyone.

Wahconah was sixteen summers old when Yonnongah, a war-hardened brave from Ossennenon in the Mohawk Valley, chanced to visit their town and stopped to pay his respects to Decanawida. He met Wahconah as she served her father's guests. His fierce eyes lit with approval as he watched her at her household chores. Enchanted by her beauty, he asked Decanawida for permission to marry her. The sage chieftain looked upon him as a brave and stalwart man, a fitting mate for his daughter. However, it was harvest time and Wahconah's services were needed to prepare food for the winter months.

256

"Come back in the spring, Yonnongah," he told the warrior. "Then shall Wahconah become your squaw."

So Yonnongah left for the Mohawk Valley, and Wahconah continued to dwell in her father's lodge.

One day Wahconah was collecting firewood in a narrow glen when she was attacked by a huge bear. Dropping the wood, the frightened girl ran, expecting at any moment to feel the sharp claws and fangs of the vicious animal, for who can outrun a bear? Suddenly a young warrior stepped into the path between her and the bear. He was an Algonquin, one of the cowardly Housatonics. In his hand he carried but a light fish spear. The fleeing Wahconah halted in amazement to see him rush at the bear with all the ferocity of a mad wolverine. The angry snarls of the beast were mingled with a loud war song from the throat of the mad warrior. Time and again the Housatonic drove his spear into the bear's body while the animal's claws tore his flesh. Finally, in a welter of blood, warrior and bear fell to the ground and lay motionless.

Wahconah, her heart beating fast, ran to the warrior and knelt beside him. He was covered with blood. His eyes were closed, but the rise and fall of his chest indicated that he lived. Gently the Mohawk maiden wiped the blood from his face. Suddenly he opened his eyes, looked up at her and smiled. She felt a flame whip her cheeks, a weakness stole through her limbs, her heart began to beat like a captured bird, and she could do nothing but trace his handsome features with her fingers. Thus did love come to Wahconah.

Presently her champion became stronger, and she helped him to his feet. Then supporting his weight, she assisted him to her father's lodge. Mohassah the Healer was summoned. He blew sweet smoke in the Algonquin's face, shook his magic rattles, placed poultices of crushed leaves on the wounds and gave him an herb broth to drink.

Meanwhile, the story of the young warrior's brave defense

of Wahconah was told throughout the town. A party of Mo-hawks carried the dead bear to the fort and everyone ex-claimed over its great size. Admiring bravery above all else, the Mohawk warriors made the Housatonic an honorary mem-ber of their Tortoise Clan, which was considered a great dis-tinction.

The young man was ill from his wounds for many days. Wahconah nursed him tenderly, feeding him with her own hands. Her beauty and tenderness captured his heart. Each day their love for each other grew stronger. He told her that his name was Nessacus, and he watched her every movement with a glance which made her weak with pleasure. When he grew stronger, he often sat in the sun by the door of the lodge.

One day Decanawida sat beside him and they talked. Nessa-cus spoke of his love for Waconah and asked the sachem for permission to marry her, promising that he would give many fine furs for her. Decanawida shook his head. He told the young Algonquin of his promise to Yonnongah.

"I am sad, for my word has been given and it is my pride that I have ever spoken with a straight tongue. You are a brave man. I would like to have you as my son—to sit beside me in the councils. It cannot be." Shaking his head sadly, he stood up and walked away.

To the lodge of the crafty Mohassah he went, and the two men smoked many pipes while they discussed the problem of the two warriors who were in love with Wahconah.

Meanwhile, Nessacus was without hope. Anger, bitterness and sorrow assailed him. In his anger he envisioned himself leading the remnants of the Housatonics in a savage and suc-cessful attack on the town, killing the Mohawk warriors and forcibly taking Wahconah as his own. In his bitterness he thought of waylaying and slaying Yonnongah, even though the act was to forfeit his own life. In his sorrow he dreamed of abducting his love and fleeing with her to some secluded glen, knowing well that both of them would be killed if they were ever after taken by the Mohawks.

With such thoughts in his mind, Nessacus grew morose and silent. His wounds healed slowly. Winter snows isolated the town and restricted travel. Wahconah, with loving attention, did everything possible to cheer him up, but in vain.

In good time the Great Manitou waved his hands over the earth and the snows and ice melted. The brown earth turned green, the south wind blew her warm breath over the lands. Birds arrived from their winter retreats. When little green ears appeared on the twigs of the beech trees, Yonnongah arrived to claim his bride. Sick with despair, Nessacus asked his host Decanawida for permission to return to his own people, but the sachem refused.

"No, my son!" he said. "Place your trust in the Great Spirit. Wahconah is still in my lodge." With these cryptic remarks, he left Nessacus.

The next day Decanawida gave a feast for Yonnongah, a feast which lasted for three days and nights. On the third evening there was a meeting of the council. The Mohawk warriors entered the longhouse of the Tortoise Clan. Women and children were excluded.

Yonnongah was introduced to the assembly as a mighty warrior.

"Hear! Hear!" the braves shouted, indicating that they wished him to speak.

Proudly Yonnongah stood up and addressed them. As was customary, he bragged of his skill as a hunter and of his bravery in many battles.

Afterward Nessacus stood before the assembly, and the scars from his fight with the bear could be seen on his face and arms.

"I am only a weak Algonquin," he said. "Once I killed a small bear." He then sat down. The Mohawks of the town laughed long and loud at his understatement, but Yonnongah scowled.

Mohassah the Healer then arose so all could heed him. Over his face was a hideous wooden mask which he wore to frighten evil spirits away. In his hands were gourd rattles, ornamented with crow's feathers. He tossed them into the air, catching them as they fell, shaking them violently until they seemed alive. He gave a wild scream and the rattles turned into birds and flew up to the smoke-covered rafters. Then he spoke. He told of the great fight between Nessacus and Mishi-mokwa, the bear. He pictured the beast as an evil demon sent to destroy the Mohawks of the town and Nessacus as their savior. "Only a mighty warrior favored by Manitou could have slain the beast," he told his audience.

He revealed Decanawida's promise to Yonnongah. "Nessacus has also asked for Wahconah. If he had not fought Mishi-mokwa, Wahconah would now be dead and Yonnongah would have had to look elsewhere for a squaw to grace his lodge. Last night while I smoked my medicine pipe, the Great Manitou came to me. His eyes were the blinding brightness of the sun. His countenance showed the wisdom of ages. His voice was like the sound of distant thunder. Over his shoulders he wore a mantle of white eagle feathers. I offered up sweet smoke to the Four Winds. Afterward he spoke to me. These are his words: 'It has come to my attention that two brave warriors yearn for the maiden Wahconah, daughter of the mighty Decanawida. One of these men would claim her on a promise; the other because he saved her life. They both have just claims. Thus only fate should judge the right. As the Mohawk are my people, this must they do. Wahconah shall be placed in a canoe without paddles at the base of the Sweetwater Falls. The canoe shall then be set adrift. In the shallow water outside the walls of this town is a small island. If the vessel bearing Wahconah passes this island on the north side, she shall belong to Yonnongah. If it passes on the south side, Nessacus will claim her. Now I have said it.' Then the Manitou turned himself into smoke and ascended through the smoke hole."

After the speech by Mohassah the Healer, the warriors voted, using short and long birch sticks for ballots. Unanimously they voted to hold the contest, as outlined to Mohassah by the Great Spirit, on the morrow. At once the braves began excitedly to bet on the results.

Yonnongah was angry but dared not oppose the wishes of his hosts. While the council members were making wagers, he slipped from the longhouse and hastened to the shore of the creek. In the bright moonlight he could see the small island in the middle of the stream. Without hesitation he waded through the shallows to the island. If the stream was obstructed on the south side, he reasoned, more water would flow on the opposite side, thus impelling the canoe to travel on the north side. He set to work throwing loose stones into the stream on the south side of the island. When he finished, most of the water was swiftly flowing on the north side. Tomorrow, Wahconah will be mine, he thought. Laughing silently, he re-entered the town.

Shortly after Yonnongah retired, a shadowy figure slipped through the town gate and hurried to the row of canoes lying on the bank of the creek. At the end of the row was an old birch canoe used by the squaws to fetch firewood. The ghostly figure dropped a bundle of furs in this canoe and returned to the darkened town.

Day's arrival was heralded by a golden-red bloom of iridescent colors in the eastern sky. The Mohawks were ready, eager to witness the contest, but certain ceremonies had to be observed. The Healer and his assistants, howling and gesturing, ran between the lodges, beating the air with bunches of feathers, thus driving away evil spirits. Water was spilled on every hearth as an offering to the River Manitou while the squaws struck marrow bones together. Yonnongah and a group of supporters walked to the north bank of the creek opposite the island. Here they squatted on the grass, playing a gambling game with a handful of knucklebones. Nessacus and members of the Tortoise Clan waded to the south shore. The inhabitants filed from the town and assembled on the banks of the stream. All eyes were watching closely as Decanawida, Mohassah and Wahconah walked to the canoes.

"Let my war canoe be used in this contest," said Decanawida.

"I am only a squaw, not worthy to ride in a war canoe," Wahconah protested. "Let me use the old squaw canoe, the birch one," she asked.

At a nod from Mohassah two warriors picked up the squaw canoe and carried it to the base of the falls. Wahconah stepped in and settled herself on a bundle of old furs.

"Watch, O Mighty Manitou," the Healer screamed, and gave the canoe a shove into the rushing waters. Like a chip, the birch canoe turned and rocked as it sped toward the island. Yonnongah and his companions forgot their game and stood up to watch the approaching craft. In the grip of the current it headed toward the north bank—and Yonnongah. Then suddenly and unexplainably, the canoe hesitated and shot to the center of the stream. It was rapidly approaching the shallows close to the island. Its course would soon be defined. Twice it grounded and each time it twisted free. And each time it moved toward the south bank. Nessacus stood on the south bank, holding his hands out toward the speeding vessel. Inexorably it headed across the shoal water. It passed the island on the south side. The Mohawks were dancing and shouting with excitement. Nessacus ran into the water and dragged the canoe ashore.

"The Great Manitou has decided," Mohassah said.

Late that afternoon Decanawida and his friend Mohassah the Healer stood on the banks of the creek watching the distant shadow that was a canoe carrying Nessacus and his bride Wah-conah to the Housatonic village. Yonnongah had left early and in a hurry for his home in the Mohawk Valley. A canoe filled with water lay several feet from the bank. Mohassah waded out and pulled it to shore. It was the squaw canoe which had carried Wahconah to the south bank. In the bottom was a bundle of soggy furs. Mohassah picked up the furs and saw a ragged hole in the bottom of the craft. From a fold in the furs, a sharp, sturdy stick fell to the ground. For a moment he looked at it. His eyes narrowed.

"A sharp stick pushed through the bottom could guide a canoe in shallow water," he observed.

Decanawida nodded agreement, and there was laughter in his voice. "The Great Manitou decided the contest—assisted by Wahconah."

Mountains of Manitou

That winter, starvation and death stalked through the village of Ay-mon-on. First bitter cold had locked the waters of the lakes and streams beneath thick, adamant ice. Next, a succession of storms had covered trails and lodges with deep drifts of snow. Then the game which the Indians depended on for subsistence—deer, moose, even the hare—had disappeared in a most mysterious manner.

At the beginning of winter each lodge had stores of corn, nuts and acorns, bear fat and dried fish. But as the severe winter advanced, tightening its icy grip over the land, these stores became depleted. The dogs were then killed and eaten. Untanned animal skins were boiled, providing thin, sour broths. People began to die. The small papoose and the elderly perished first. Squaws and braves, weakened by hunger, found increasing difficulty in collecting the wood needed to keep the lodges warm.

In the wigwam of the Sachem Pannake, death had been a visitor. His little daughter had died. His wife of many years lay on a bear robe. She had covered her face. Soon death would enter the lodge again—and she would die.

Then spoke the sachem's son, Hokkomando, a youth of sixteen summers.

"I will not sit here and wait for death. Better to meet it while hunting for food. I am still strong. Tomorrow I will hunt to the south. If I kill game, I shall return with meat. If not, you will not look upon me again."

Pannake, huddled close to the earth, nodded agreement. "So be it," he said.

In the half light of dawn, Hokkomando slipped on his snowshoes and trudged through the drifts toward the south. Overhead the cold, blue, sweeping fingers of the aurora borealis cast weird lights and shadows over the surface of the snow. Playful gusts of wind circled, whipping up small clouds of snowflakes which whirled madly for a moment before falling back to the drifts.

For several hours the hunter walked toward the south without sighting another living creature. The earth was dead, dead under a white shroud. The snowshoes dragged on his legs and hunger cramps forced him to rest often. After a time his strength deserted him and he fell into a deep drift. I am about to die, he thought. Instead he slept. In his sleep he saw a vision. He saw a beautiful mountain country where birds, beasts and fruit were plentiful.

His vision passed. He awoke and staggered to his feet. His despairing eyes could see nothing but the grim, frozen wilderness. He was in a pitiful plight. His bow and spear were lost, buried somewhere in the snow. His hands were like pieces of ice, and the cold was penetrating his clothing. The next time he fell, he would arise no more. In weak anger he raised his clenched fists toward the sky.

"Great Manitou!" he cried. "Where is this wonderful country I have seen. Why do you mock me? Why show me these wonders if I am about to die?"

The snow suddenly swirled about him, blinding him. Behind the screen of billowing flakes he sensed the presence of the Great Spirit.

"Take these, my son!" a deep voice spoke. "You shall live and become the benefactor of your people."

Into Hokkomando's hands he thrust a spear and a burning coal. The coal burned his hand, and the young hunter dropped it on the ground. Instantly the snow melted and the rocks began to burn, sending up dense clouds of smoke and steam. The fire spread and the earth trembled. Then came the voice of the Great Spirit out of the smoke and flames, bidding mountains to arise. The earth heaved and shook. Through the reek, the youth saw hills lifting—lifting until their tops were hidden in the clouds. From the summits came the deep sound of Manitou's voice.

"These great White Mountains will be my home. Here I shall live and watch over my children."

As Hokkomando stared in wonder, the smoke and steam receded. Streams burst forth from the rocks and cascaded down the mountainsides in a thousand brooks and rills. The air grew warm, and spring arrived in a moment. Bushes and grass grew. Birds sang. And in mountain glades herds of deer browsed.

A giant moose appeared and the young hunter, remembering his mission, pursued it. The animal set off at a trot northward, toward the snow-bound village of Ay-mon-on. As quarry and hunter left the vicinity of the newly created mountains, they again entered a land of winter. Tenaciously Hokkomando followed the great beast. In time he reached the top of a hill and saw the snow-covered lodges of his people. The moose headed toward the middle of the village, and the young hunter knew that this was as Manitou willed. Running to the side of the animal, he slew it with the spear.

The people of Ay-mon-on were saved from starvation by the flesh of the moose. A few days later, winter fled before the warm onslaught of spring. Game and fish became plentiful. The Indians grew strong again.

One day the village of Ay-mon-on was abandoned. The

people, dragging their possessions on travois, followed Hokko-mando to the south. Presently they came to a beautiful country populated by vast numbers of deer and moose. Lush grass and woodlands grew in fertile valleys and intervales. High over-head towered the peaks of the White Mountains. As they paused to gaze at their future homes, they heard the voice of Manitou.

"You are my people and this is your land."

Bibliography

Barber, John Warner. *Barber's Historical Collection of Connecticut.* New Haven: Durrie & Peck, 1856.

Bicknell, Thomas Williams. *The History of the State of Rhode Island and Providence Plantations.* Vol. 3. New York: The American Historical Society Inc., 1920.

Botkin, B. A., compiler and editor. *A Treasury of American Folklore.* New York: Crown Publishers, 1944.

Bradford, William. *Bradford's History of Plimoth Plantation.* Boston: Wright & Potter Printing Company, 1898.

Cathorne-Hardy, G. M. *The Norse Discoverers of America.* London: Oxford, Clarendon Press, 1921.

Caverly, Robert B. *Heroism of Hannah Dustin.* Boston: B. B. Russell & Company, 1875.

Chase, George Wingate. *The History of Haverhill.* Haverhill: Published by the author.

Collins, Edward Day. *A History of Vermont.* Boston: Ginn & Company, 1903.

Crawford, Mary C. *St. Botolph's Town.* Boston: L. C. Page & Company, 1908.

Delabarre, Edmund Burke. *Dighton Rock.* New York: W. Neale, 1928.

——. *Recent History of Dighton Rock.* Cambridge, Mass.: J. Wilson and Son.

Drake, Samuel Adams. *A Book of New England Legends and Folklore.* Boston: Little, Brown and Company, 1910.

——. *History of Middlesex County, Massachusetts.* Boston: Estes & Lauriat, 1880.

English, J. S. *Indian Legends of the White Mountains.* Boston: Rand, Avery, 1915.

Fisher, Dorothy Canfield. *Vermont Tradition.* Boston: Little, Brown and Company, 1953.

Fiske, John. *The Discovery of America.* Vol. 1. Boston: Houghton, Mifflin & Company, 1894.

Gomez, Isabel. "Rogers' Rangers at St. Francis." *Vermont History Magazine.* Montpelier, Vermont: Vermont Historical Society, Oct. 1959.

Goodwin, John A. *Pilgrim Republic.* Boston: Houghton, Mifflin and Company, 1899.

Goodwin, William B. *The Ruins of Great Ireland in New England.* Boston: Meador Publishing Company, 1946.

Haklukt, Richard. *Voyages of the Elizabethan Seaman to America.* London: Oxford, The Clarendon Press, 1893.

Haley, John W. *The Old Stone Bank History of Rhode Island.* Providence: The Providence Institution for Savings, 1939.

Haugen, Einar. *Voyages to Vinland.* New York: A. A. Knopf, 1942.

Hawes, Heldreth G. *The Bellamy Treasure.* Augusta, Maine: The Augusta Press, 1940.

Holbrook, Stewart H. *Ethan Allen.* New York: The Macmillan Company, 1940.

Holden, Raymond P. *The Merrimack.* New York: Rinehart & Company, Inc., 1958.

Holmes, Herbert Edgar. *The Makers of Maine.* Lewiston, Maine: The Haswell Press, 1912.

Hunt, Edmund S. *Weymouth Ways and Weymouth People.* Boston: Private printing.

Jameson, John Franklin. *Privateering and Piracy in the Colonial Period.* New York: The Macmillan Company, 1923.

Kirke, Edmund. "The Haunted House at Watertown." *Harper's New Monthly Magazine.* Vol. 35. New York: Harper & Brothers, 1867.

Lightfoot, Captain. *An Autobiography.* Topsfield, Massachusetts: The Wayside Press, 1926.

Morrison, Mary Gray. "A Puritan Indeed." *Harper's New Monthly Magazine.* Vol. 71. New York: Harper & Brothers, 1885.

Morton, Thomas. *New England Canaan.* Boston: Prince Society, 1883.

Northend, Mary H. *Historic Homes of New England.* Boston: Little, Brown & Company, 1914.

Peattie, Roderick. Compiled and edited. *The Berkshires.* New York: The Vanguard Press Inc., 1948.

Pell, John. *Ethan Allen.* Boston: Houghton, Mifflin Company, 1929.

Reman, Edward. *The Norse Discoveries and Explorations in America.* University of California Press, 1949.

Rogers, Mary Cockrane. *Glimpses of an Old Social Capitol, Portsmouth.* Boston: Merrymount Press, 1934.

Rose, Mrs. Melvin (Maizie). *Block Island Scrapbook.* New York: Pageant Press, Inc., 1957.

Scott, Kenneth. *Counterfeiting in Colonial America.* New York: Oxford University Press, 1957.

Skinner, Charles M. *Myths and Legends of our Own Land.* Philadelphia: J. P. Lippincott Company, 1896.

Stackpole, Everett S. *History of New Hampshire.* New York: American Historical Society, 1916.

Tilton, George H. *A History of Rehoboth, Massachusetts.* Boston: Published by the author, 1918.

Todd, Charles Burr. *Old Connecticut Path.* New York: The Grafton Press, 1906.

Tourtellot, Arthur B. *The Charles.* New York: Farrar & Rinehart, 1941.

Town Meeting Book, Lyme (Conn.) Records, 1664.

Verrill, A. Hyatt. *Romantic and Historic Maine.* New York: Dodd, Mead & Company, 1933.

Weston, Thomas. *A History of Middleborough (Mass.).* Boston: Houghton, Mifflin Company, 1906.

Workers of the Federal Writers' Project. *Berkshire Hills.* New York: Funk & Wagnalls, 1939.

——. *Connecticut.* Boston: Houghton, Mifflin Company, 1938.

——. *Maine.* Boston: Houghton, Mifflin Company, 1937.

——. *Massachusetts.* Boston: Houghton, Mifflin Company, 1937.

——. *Rhode Island.* Boston: Houghton, Mifflin Company, 1937.

——. *Vermont.* Boston: Houghton, Mifflin Company, 1937.